The Animals in the Bible

The Frontiers of Knowledge Series

"One consequence of the rise of the American university graduate school with its strong emphasis upon advanced study and research has been the growing separation of first-rank scholars and scientists from the task of presenting their own subjects in primary and secondary schools—indeed even in elementary courses for undergraduates.

"The chief contact between those on the frontiers of scholarship and students in schools was through the occasional textbooks for high schools prepared by such distinguished scientists as Millikin or by historians of the stature of Beard or Commager. For the most part, however, the scholars at the forefront of their disciplines, those who might be able to make the greatest contribution to the substantive reorganization of their fields, were not involved in the development of curricula for the schools. In consequence, school programs have often dealt inadequately or incorrectly with contemporary knowledge. . . ." So reports Dr. Jerome S. Bruner in his recent book THE PROCESS OF EDUCATION.

This statement and many similar calls for action establish the need for the new "Frontiers of Knowledge" series under which Chilton Books will publish titles in various disciplines. The content will be accurate and up-to-date, readable and challenging, and it will be presented *effectively*, with proper regard not only for coverage, but also for *structure*.

Grasping the *structure* of a subject is understanding it in a way that permits many other things to be meaningfully related to it. To learn *structure* is, essentially, to learn how things are related. This type of presentation has a desirable effect on attitudes because it allows for growth in the method of *discovery*—the exciting sequence that leads a student to *discover* for himself.

To accomplish its purpose, Chilton Books, in the "Frontiers of Knowledge" series, will include titles in *unexplored* areas of knowledge as well as in familiar areas. These may include investigation of "borderlands" such as abominable snowmen and planetoids, but they will also cover such *untreated* subjects as the natural science of the animals in the Bible, how an oceanarium operates, the history of the Great Wall of China, and many others. But all of the titles, whether they are on traditional or untrod ground, will contain the most recent discoveries and/or research data *whether or not* they have yet been *accepted* in orthodox academic circles.

All of the books will have extensive bibliographies, detailed and specially developed indexes, tables of contents, maps, illustrations, and appendices. They will be attractively designed, printed on top-grade paper stock, and bound in library-type bindings for durability. Reasonably priced, these important books will be a major contribution to American education.

The
ANIMALS
in the
BIBLE

The Identity and Natural History of All
the Animals Mentioned in the Bible

by

ROY PINNEY

With a Collection of Photographs
of Living Species Taken in the
Holy Land by the Author

CHILTON BOOKS

A Division of Chilton Company
Publishers
Philadelphia and New York

Introduction

"And God blessed them, and God said unto them, Be fruitful, and multiply, and replenish the earth, and subdue it: and have dominion over the fish of the sea, and over the fowl of the air, and over every living thing that moveth upon the earth."

(Gen. 1:28)

"And out of the ground the Lord God formed every beast of the field, and every fowl of the air; and brought *them* unto Adam to see what he would call them: and whatsoever Adam called every living creature, that *was* the name thereof."

(Gen. 2:19)

As mathematicians and physicists work to piece together a picture of the future, men of other disciplines and sciences are having equal success in reconstructing and recalling the past. The most dramatic progress made by the latter group has included filling in the details of man's early adventures as recorded in the Bible.

Within recent years, archaeological discoveries, the recovery of dead languages, and refinements in the science of philology have permitted the Bible to be read as a testament in other than merely religious terms. Each year, scientists and scholars come forward with further corroboration of the Bible's historical accuracy.

We have identified the tiny scaled creatures which made up the miraculous "manna" that appeared like dew each morning to feed the Children of Israel on their march through the Wilderness of Zin. We know which fishes were harvested by the Apostles of Jesus from their nets in the Sea of Galilee; which animals and birds were prescribed by Mosaic law to be offered up for sacrifice by the priests in the Holy Temple of Solomon some three thousand years ago.

One fascinating aspect of this recovery of the past—up to now not made available to the general public—has been an identification to a high degree of accuracy of the animal life that figures in the pastoral and agricultural setting of the Biblical world. Improved readings of the basic texts in Hebrew, reinforced by a knowledge of the languages of the surrounding peoples—such as Ugaritic, Akkadian, Sumerian, and Egyptian—now permit the reader to know with a great measure of accuracy the fauna of those early days. Preserved in the Bible is a detailed panorama of the animal life of the Near East of millennia ago.

v

The animal life of Biblical times persists to this day. It is not a matter of restoring Sumerian ziggurats on the plains of Mesopotamia, or digging hundreds of feet below the earth to find the lost cities of Jericho. The spider that spun a protective web across the cave in which David hid from the soldiers of the angry King Saul has not been trampled by the march of history. The sheep and the goats that were herded by the nomad, Jacob, continue in the flocks of wandering Bedouins today. The falcon, the eagle, the night hawk, and the lapwing have proved more enduring than the mighty palace of Darius or the tombs of the Pharaohs.

This book presents the integrated evaluations of the latest findings of the archaeologist, the philologist, and the zoologist with respect to the animal world of the Bible. It is at once a literary appreciation of Biblical history and an authentic photographic concordance to the Bible.

ROY PINNEY

Contents

The Animals in the Bible

Names and Order of All the Books of the Bible, with the Number of Their Chapters

BOOKS OF THE OLD TESTAMENT

Genesis	50	Ecclesiastes	12
Exodus	40	Song of Solomon	8
Leviticus	27	Isaiah	66
Numbers	36	Jeremiah	52
Deuteronomy	34	Lamentations	5
Joshua	24	Ezekiel	48
Judges	21	Daniel	12
Ruth	4	Hosea	14
I Samuel	31	Joel	3
II Samuel	24	Amos	9
I Kings	22	Obadiah	1
II Kings	25	Jonah	4
I Chronicles	29	Micah	7
II Chronicles	36	Nahum	3
Ezra	10	Habakkuk	3
Nehemiah	13	Zephaniah	3
Esther	10	Haggai	2
Job	42	Zechariah	14
Psalms	150	Malachi	4
Proverbs	31		

BOOKS OF THE NEW TESTAMENT

Matthew	28	I Timothy	6
Mark	16	II Timothy	4
Luke	24	Titus	3
John	21	Philemon	1
The Acts	28	Hebrews	13
Romans	16	James	5
I Corinthians	16	I Peter	5
II Corinthians	13	II Peter	3
Galatians	6	I John	5
Ephesians	6	II John	1
Philippians	4	III John	1
Colossians	4	Jude	1
I Thessalonians	5	Revelation	22
II Thessalonians	3		

Chapter 1
Lands of the Bible

If you were on a tropical isle, in the midst of a steaming jungle surrounded by vines and palm trees, you would be surprised if you came across a polar bear. If you were walking in a desert you would not expect to meet a chimpanzee.

At any particular place you have a fair idea of what kinds of animals you will encounter. That is because almost all species of animals are specially adapted to the many factors that may be lumped together in the word "environment." Each kind of animal can survive in a land only when the right physical conditions *for it* exist: there must be the correct food; the correct weather, neither too hot nor too cold, neither too wet nor too dry; the correct terrain—mountain, forest, or desert—and so on. And if the environment should change for any reason, then the animals living there must either adapt—which means change their own physical natures, thus becoming different animals—or die out, at least locally.

Think, for example, of what happened to the dinosaurs. Once the lords of the earth, these enormous creatures perished when the environment which supported them changed, and new animals, better suited to the new conditions, replaced them. Think of all the elements needed to make life possible for a robin or a sparrow: warm temperatures, nesting materials, trees, a supply of berries, worms, and other foods, which in turn require for their existence fertile soil, water, etc. Such a list of survival factors can be drawn up for any animal—mammal, bird, reptile, fish, or insect.

Only man seems to have conquered his environment by building fires and shelters for warmth, by digging holes for water, by irrigating a desert for food, and so on, and thus can survive in all climates; but, even then, surviving, in some climates, can be accomplished only through the most extreme efforts.

The lands forming the setting for the Bible comprise regions of southwestern Asia and northeastern Africa equaling an area in the United States from Maryland to Florida, and from the Atlantic to the Mississippi. They are peculiarly rich in animal life because within this relatively small region can be found many different environments. These range from arid deserts to dank marshlands, from grassy plains to icy mountain peaks, from moist fertile lands to sand-strewn wastelands, from clear rivers to the Dead Sea. An examination of these lands will provide a background for the discussions of the Bible's animals.

1

The Bible's lands, where the first stirrings of Western civilization took place, include the Nile River area in Egypt; the valleys of the Tigris and the Euphrates Rivers which are now part of Iraq, but which were known in ancient times as Mesopotamia ("Land Between Two Rivers"); and the territories which make up the modern countries of Syria and Lebanon, the northern part of Saudi Arabia, Jordan, and Israel.

The Middle (or, more correctly, the Near) East, as this area is now known, is of immense importance because it links the continents of Europe, Asia, and Africa. The cultures which were born here spread in all three directions. In particular, the area known until recently as Palestine was the crossroads of the ancient world. People (and animals) traveling between Egypt and Mesopotamia, and later between Europe and Asia, could not cross the vast Arabian desert, and so had to follow a route which led through Syria and along the coast of Palestine, an area of rich soil known as the "Fertile Crescent."

The country of Palestine, and its neighbor, Transjordan, no longer exist. In 1947, the United Nations agreed to split the area into two nations: Israel, a country for the Jews, and Jordan, a country for the Arabs, the latter incorporating all of ancient Transjordan, plus a chunk of territory on the western side of the Jordan bulging toward Beersheba. The coastal lands—excepting the strategic Gaza Strip—and all the fertile regions were given to Israel.

Through the fertile crescent of Palestine there flows twice every year a great tide of birds and animals on the move. To avoid unfavorable environments caused by changing seasons, many animals, birds in particular, migrate, moving to warmer lands in the winter and to cooler ones in the summer. The migrations of most of the area's creatures take them through Palestine, some remaining for an entire season there, others only passing through. Almost every species of bird to be found in northern Africa, southern Europe including the Mediterranean regions, and western Asia can be found at one time or another in Palestine. Thus, the geographically central Bible lands have their animal life periodically enriched.

The climate of Palestine, which determines the flora and fauna of the area, is produced by the interplay of geographical factors. Located in the warm temperate belt (29° to 33° north latitude), its proximity to the Mediterranean spares it the aridness of the interior areas of Arabia and Syria. With the exception of the Jordan River valley, the temperatures of the region rarely exceed 90° Fahrenheit, and in February, in the middle of the Palestinian winter, the mean temperature ranges in the vicinity of 45°.

There is no true winter as we know it; rather, there is a rainy season and a dry one. The rainy season, equivalent to winter, begins in November when the warm winds from the sea are cooled as they meet the mountain air. The winds deposit their moisture in the strip of Israel and then continue on to the Jordan River where, warmed once again, they take up new moisture to soak the tablelands beyond, making the land fertile, and swelling the many small streams which flow into the Jordan River. In March the torrents subside, and by May the mountain air no longer is cold enough to produce rain. This season is a time of harvest; the farmer's ripened crops must be gathered quickly before the hot, dry summer begins. During the summer months, June to September, the heat during the day, especially in the interior regions, occasionally becomes intolerable for man and beast alike, but because of the dryness the evenings are pleasantly cool.

The greatly varying temperatures and humidities of Palestine, of course, have their effect on the animal life. At times, when conditions reach their extremes, the mortality rate of some species increases greatly. In the rainy season, for example, small rodents and their predators—jackals, foxes, birds of prey, and snakes—are forced to migrate from the low-lying lands to the drier mountain regions; in the dry season a reverse migration takes place. Similar phenomena can be observed in other species.

Bird migrations of various species take place almost throughout the year, but the bulk occur in March and April. In the spring and autumn months fierce, hot winds called "sirocco," or "hamsins," blow across the land from the deserts. The wind wilts flowers, shrivels leaves, blackens plants, and sweeps flocks of insects and birds from the sky. Animals who cannot find shelter from the heat and sun die. These extremes do not affect the entire land, for climatic conditions vary from region to region, depending upon other factors.

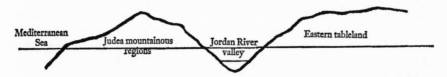

Mediterranean Sea — Judea mountainous regions — Jordan River valley — Eastern tableland

The accompanying diagram presents a typical cross section of Israel and Western Jordan. It shows the mountainous region of Judea (formerly an elevated tableland pressed together, so to speak, by rainfall and erosion), the deep depression of the Jordan River valley, and a second tableland, or plateau, to the east which is somewhat flatter than the mountainous region. As the diagram shows, the central and dominating factor of the land is the Jordan River and its valley which, lying well below sea level, is the deepest depression scooped out anywhere on land by nature. The river is the most important influence upon the climate and plant growth of the area, and thus the most important factor in the land's animal distribution. An imaginary journey down the river would therefore be in order.

At the northern end of the Jordan Valley, where the borders of Syria and Lebanon meet, stands Mt. Hermon. On the eastern side the mountain slope is steep and almost barren of plant life, while, on the western slope, grow some evergreens and wild fruit trees. Hermon is covered with snow from 2800 feet up to its peak at 9000 feet during the winter but by September very little remains. The mountain's bare white stones can be seen as far away as Bethlehem's hills; because it dominates the landscape for many miles the Arabs call Hermon *Jebel esh Sheikh*, Sheikh Mountain, "chief of mountains." It is from the vicinity of Mt. Hermon that the Jordan River begins its descent.

Four tributaries and a number of small streams from the grotto of Paneas join to form the Jordan River and the neighboring River of Paneas (named after the Greek nature-god Pan). As these streams swell the river, the waters plunge southward with great force, eventually reaching a swampy area. This area in ancient times was the source of papyrus, a reed-like plant used to make mats and rolls of writing material. (The word "paper" stems from papyrus.) The waters flow through this land and into a shallow lake known in Biblical times as Semechonitis, today called Lake Huleh. Emerging from Lake Huleh as rapids, the water rushes 10 miles into the Sea of Galilee (also known as the Lake of Tiberias), a descent of 689 feet to a depth of 682 feet below sea level. Galilee remains, as it was thousands of years ago, a rich source of fish for the inhabitants of the land.

Leaving Galilee the Jordan twists like a snake through the deepest valley in the world, some 65 miles (200 miles if we follow the tortuous river route) to the Dead Sea, 1286 feet below sea level. Along this route the river valley widens from 4 to 14 miles, and slopes up to heights of 3000 feet in the surrounding country. The western side of the valley is rather dry, with little rainfall and few tributaries; few areas are fit settlements for men or animals. A notable exception is the city of Jericho in Jordan.

To the east, on the other hand, the Yarmouk River and many smaller streams provide large areas of fertile land. Within the valley itself there is a strip of still further depressed land which once was heavily forested. In these forests, parts of which still remain, many wild animals once roamed. The Bible refers to this area in Jer. 49:19: "Behold, he shall come up like a lion from the swelling of Jordan . . ."

The Jordan River ends in the Dead Sea, one of the most remarkable natural formations in the world. Each of the ancient peoples had a different name for this body of water, each name expressive of one of the sea's unique qualities. To the Greeks, for example, it was known as "Asphalt Lake" because of the asphalt which now and then floats to its surface and washes up on its shores. The Hebrews call it the "Sea of Salt." Its extreme saltiness results from the great amount of evaporation from the lake itself and from the rivers which feed it—evaporation caused by the torrid sun and dry air. Modern man calls it the Dead Sea because almost nothing can live in its saline waters. South of the Dead Sea there is a marshy area called *es Sebkha* ("land on which a salt crust has formed"), which, like the sea itself, is barren. From *es Sebkha*, stretching a hundred miles south to the Gulf of Aqaba in the Red Sea, lie nothing but arid desert wastelands.

Between the valley and the Mediterranean which licks the western shores of Israel lies the coastal plain, an area in contrast to the Jordan Valley in that it is consistently fertile. The plain stretches from Egypt to Lebanon, and varies in width from 12 miles near the city of Gaza (not to be confused with the Gaza Strip) to 200 yards at the promontory of Mt. Carmel, near Haifa. Around Gaza the land is rich, a "garden spot" containing springs, regal sycamore trees, flourishing olive groves, and, consequently, a nice assortment of animals.

Although the lands of the Bible contain many different types of terrain, generally speaking the area can be divided into three broad zones: forest, steppe, and desert, each zone having its own climate, its own forms of vegetation (or lack of vegetation), and, therefore, its own species of animal life.

Running along Israel's coastline, along the border with Egypt down to the Gulf of Aqaba and then up again toward the Dead Sea, there is a uniform strip of desert. Reaching up into the Jordan Valley, the sand dunes also cover most of the eastern part of Jordan. Dry as these deserts are, except for the salted regions near the Dead Sea, they are not at all lifeless. As well as being dotted with oases, the desert contains its own forms of animal and vegetable life which have adjusted to the scarcity of water. Over the centuries, much of the desert's vegetation has provided fodder for man's camels and fuel for his fires.

Within the desert strip lie the forest lands and steppes which cover most of Palestine. Long ago, at the beginning of the Neolithic age, vast forests covered much of the land. The Plain of Sharon which extends northward from the city of Jaffa was such an area, and because the dunes near the sea held back the water from the hills to the east, it was dotted with swamps as well. Another forest zone was the area called Gilead in the Old Testament; once a rich mass of oaks, Gilead has been cut through with valleys formed by the large amount of rainfall. Today, in the area of the Neolithic forest zones, the land has few trees and is covered mostly by bare rocks and hills.

The fact that a geographical area is a forest zone can be determined by measuring the amount of rainfall. A forest zone, for example, in the latitude of Palestine receives 12 to 14 or more inches of rain annually, while a desert gets less than eight. The annual amount of rainfall on the steppe regions falls between these two values. The existence of a forest zone can also be determined by the flowers that blossom forth from crevices, in the spring. The forest climate with its substantial rainfall produces anenomes, ranunculi, alpine violets, iris, orchids, and asphodel.

The forests of the Biblical regions gave way before the encroachments of men, just as the vast forests of the American continent did later. Biblical life centered about the raising of goats and sheep. To provide their flocks with grazing land the shepherds and goatherds cut down the forests. As late as 1900, some forest still remained in east Jordan, but even that has since disappeared. Once the forests were gone soil erosion set in, and today most of the soil in these regions has been washed away, leaving the hillsides covered with bare white rock. Where once the land flourished with evergreen oak, deciduous oak, and Neppopines, today only small Macchi-bushes struggle to survive. (Happily, under the careful irrigation of the Hebrews who have returned to their homeland, some forest regions are now beginning to bloom with wheat fields and olive orchards.)

Between the desert and the forests, roughly enclosing all of Israel and western Jordan except for the northern region, there are the steppes, those mountainous regions which cover much of Palestine. A steppe is considered a region which cannot support a forest. Grasses, bushes, and occasionally trees do grow, however. The steppes were used for grazing in Biblical times. Extending southward from the valley of the Leontes, the steppes slope downward sharply into the Jordan Valley. In the west their central area is called Samaria, a region less rugged than the Galilee country, with gentle hills and valleys. Moving southward the steppes stretch over the area of Judea as a high, mountainous plateau. The city of Jerusalem lies in a depression within Judea. South of Jerusalem the plateau rises again to the high areas north of Hebron (3370 feet above sea level).

East of Judea there is a sudden drop in three terraces into the Dead Sea. As the steppe descends it reaches a desolate area of gorges, canyons and bare rock called in the Old Testament "the wilderness of Judea." East of the Jordan the land rises again to the high tableland mentioned earlier. In the north there is a land called Hagolan containing volcanic hills and craters. To the south the disintegration of lava deposits has left a more fertile region, called Bashan in Biblical days. Bashan was once a forest land of oak trees well suited to cattle breeding. South of Bashan is the forest land of Gilead, and still farther south is a ridge running from the Jabbok. The land of the Ammonites lies east of this ridge, while to the south, below the River Arnon, lies the land on which the kingdom of Moab once stood.

This, then, is the land of the Bible, a land where camels find their proper environment along with fish, birds, and oxen. Here dwell hares and swine, wild goats and cats, gazelles and dogs, snakes and antelope, each finding in some region, be it desert, steppe, or forest, its proper *environment*—the proper set of conditions in which each can survive and thrive.

Each left its mark, for good or bad, on the men who dwelled in Palestine thousands of years ago; each found its little niche in the record of those men—the record we call the Bible.

Chapter 2
Origin of the Bible

For almost 3000 years, men have been fascinated by the Bible. The famous stories of the creation of the world and the creation of man, of the great Israelite patriarchs, of Moses and the flight from Egypt, of David and Solomon and Daniel, were first sung, then told by fathers to their children. They were told and retold until they were finally written down on dried animal hides, or papyrus, or parchment, or clay tablets, or paper, to be read, studied, memorized.

The Bible has been discussed, interpreted, translated, commented upon, written about, counted, reprinted, and then read some more. Originally the document of religion for the small nomadic tribe of the Israelites, it has become Holy Writ for four major religions—Jewish, Catholic, Protestant, and Islamic—embracing hundreds of different beliefs among half the world's people.

Nations have fought bloody wars over their interpretations of the Bible. Even men of the same belief will spend weeks, even years, debating the meaning of a single passage. Some people have accepted every word in the Bible as literal truth, believing that the earth was, indeed, created in seven days, and that Adam was the first man, and that the serpent tempted Eve, and that Noah alone was saved from a great flood, and that the Red Sea split in two to allow the Children of Israel to pass through. Others have tried to interpret the Bible in the light of science, saying that the Biblical stories are allegories, that their meaning is not to be taken literally but symbolically. Still others have denied the Bible, calling it mere literature—the myth and superstition of a primitive people. No matter what men have felt about the Bible, they have never ignored it. It stands unchallenged as a writing of immense literary worth as well as a central document of civilization as we know it.

To understand how the Bible came to such prominence, we must go back to the beginning. You may be familiar with the story of the blind poet Homer—how, as minstrel to the great Greek kings, he sang the stories of Achilles and Odysseus, of the 10-year war at Troy, and of the Olympian gods, stories which he or someone later wrote down in *The Iliad* and *The Odyssey*, works which later became the "bible" of ancient Greek civilization.

The Old Testament was born in much the same way. A man, whom scholars call "J" because his name has been lost over the years (he is called "J" because he uses the name "Yahweh" or "Jehovah" in referring to God), apparently sang the traditional stories of Israelite history in about 850 B.C. To a gathering of his people, perhaps in an oasis or around a well, "J" sang the familiar tales of the Israelite heroes, Abraham, Joseph, and Moses, of their wars and hardships, of their God and their glory in being the "Chosen People." "J" was a poet who put into verse the well-known heritage of his people, and eventually the verses were copied down. About a century later, a man known as "E" (because he used the title "Elohim" for God) retold "J" 's stories, adding to them, enriching and enlarging them, and pointing morals. From these stories there began to emerge a form, a theme. The talented men who reworked the stories were forming a work of art, a book, something that would endure. In later times a group of priests, called "P" by the scholars, used the framework of legend and history collected by "J" and "E" as the basis for a system of law.

At last the Bible as we know it was emerging. Like the recognizable form that is developed from a lump of clay by the sculptor's skillful fingers, the priests brought from their mass of writings a theme—the Covenant. The Covenant, the basis of the Jewish religion, is an agreement between God and his people, the Children of Israel, promising eternal blessedness in return for obedience. It is what binds the Israelites to God.

The Bible, as it finally emerged, tells us what led up to the Covenant (Genesis), how the Covenant was established through Moses (Exodus), what the Covenant contained (Leviticus and Deuteronomy), what happened to the Covenant (the books of history such as Joshua), how the Covenant was celebrated (Psalms), and how it fell into neglect and was later revived (the books of the prophets, such as Isaiah and Ezekiel). In the years which followed, other writers added to the Bible. We know, for example, that in the court of David a man known to us as Abiather, who was an historian, added the chronicles of the Judaic kings to the history of the Children of Israel. The New Testament, which is accepted as part of the Bible by Catholics and Protestants but not by Jews, begins at a time a little after the end of the Old Testament and tells the story of Jesus Christ, who Christians believe was born to establish a new Covenant.

The Old Testament was written mostly in Hebrew, the ancient language of the Israelites, on dried animal skins or parchments which were sewn together and rolled up on rods to form scrolls. The tradition has been kept to this day, and in synagogues you will find Torahs—scrolls of law written in Hebrew on parchment scrolls. The Torah contains the Pentateuch, the first five books of the Bible. A few parts were written in Aramaic, a Semitic language which came into use among the Israelites during their exile in Babylon. The writers of the New Testament, on the other hand, wrote in Greek (with the single exception of Matthew, who wrote in Aramaic), the language widely used by the civilized world following the conquests of Alexander the Great. Thus we can see how the Bible came to be so significant: first, as the history of a nation and the statement of the beliefs of that nation; and, more importantly, as a book of faith and moral law for millions of people of all races, nationalities, and creeds.

The books of the Bible fall naturally into three categories: those dealing primarily with history, those dealing with law, and those dealing with prophecy. Taken together, they form a source of religious inspiration and belief as well as one of the truly remarkable literary achievements of all time.

Men have approached the Bible in many different ways, some of which may surprise you. A short time ago, for example, an oil company used certain passages from the Bible to locate an oil well in the Middle East, thus demonstrating the great accuracy of the Scriptures both historically and geographically.

Despite the comparatively primitive means of transmission used to pass the Bible down through the generations, the text we have today seems to be remarkably close to the original. This fact was pointed up by the discovery recently of a group of writings, called the Dead Sea Scrolls, which somehow escaped the traditional destruction of temple manuscripts, because of age. The Dead Sea Scrolls, which were inscribed on thin sheets of copper, were found in large earthen pots, and buried in caves in the desert, where the dryness prevented them from disintegrating, thus remaining the oldest surviving Biblical manuscripts. They have as yet been only partially examined by Bible experts and scholars, but the comparisons with modern versions which have been completed show remarkably little difference. The Bible we read today, therefore, is substantially the same as that read two thousand years ago.

Another way men have approached the Bible is to look for more than is already there, seeking anagrams and riddles and secret messages through bizarre codes. From the "secrets" they find in the Bible by, for example, taking the first letters of each chapter and rearranging them to form words, they develop mystical religions and cults.

Perhaps no book has ever been examined as closely as the Bible. Men have even taken the time and effort to count all the various things it contains. Their mathematical endeavors have revealed such sidelights as: there are 1189 chapters in the Bible, of which 979 are in the Old Testament. The middle chapter of the Bible is Psalm 117 (being both preceded and followed by 594 chapters), which happens also to be the shortest chapter of the Bible, 28 words in all. Going farther, the counters have added up 31,173 verses in the Bible, of which 23,214 are in the Old Testament, and 773,692 words, of which 559,439 are in the Old Testament.

Although there are over three-quarters of a million words in the

Bible, there are only about 7000 *different* words, the most common being the word "and," which appears 46,227 times in the Scriptures. There are 3,566,480 single letters in the Bible, give or take a few, and the longest word is "Mahershalalhashbaz," which has 18 letters. (Mahershalalhashbaz is the transliteration of a Hebrew sentence which means literally, "The booty hastens; the spoil speeds." It refers to a prophecy of doom for Syria.)

The first Bible was printed by Johannes Gutenberg, the German who built the first printing press in 1456. In fact, the Bible was the first book ever run off on this epochal invention. Since then more than a *billion* copies of the Scriptures have been printed. The Bible has been translated into 180 languages and dialects, with substantial portions of it being translated into an additional 1100. Each year 8 or 10 languages are added to the list. The first Bible translated and printed in North America was in the language of the Algonquin Indians. The Puritans who settled in America brought their English editions with them from England, of course, but in 1661 they decided that their Indian neighbors should be able to share in the general enlightenment.

There have been literally hundreds of English versions of the Bible. The most widespread is the King James version, which is used by most Protestants. In 1919, the Jewish version, the standard text for English-speaking Jews, was put together. Catholics use the Confraternity version, the Douay-Rheims, or the Westminster edition. While basically the same, the various differences in translation of these Bibles reflect the dissimilar interpretations of faith of these religions.

Besides the standard editions, many unusual versions of the Bible have been printed over the years. There is, for example, a translation known as the Breeches Bible. Printed in England some time ago, this version tells how, after Adam and Eve ate the forbidden fruit, they gathered fig leaves and fashioned "breeches" to cover themselves. Thomas Jefferson, third President of the United States and author of the Declaration of Independence, attempted to improve the Scriptures by rearranging many passages. His work on what is called the Jefferson Bible was never finished. In addition, idiosyncrasies of translation have given us a Bug Bible, an Idle Bible, a Printer's Bible, and so on.

Several centuries ago, a new copy of a Bible was brought to the king of England for inspection. He promptly called it the Wicked Bible and ordered the entire printing destroyed. Some copies of the Wicked Bible, however, still exist, and if you read one you would be as shocked as the king when you came to the Seventh Commandment. Because of a typographical error it reads: "Thou shalt commit adultery."

The Bible is the most fascinating book ever written. No matter how we accept it, it is a work of consummate art and genius, always fresh, and always full of surprises for those who know it well.

Chapter 3
Animal Worship

Most ancient societies worshiped animals, animal images, or gods who assumed the form of animals. The Hindus, for example, believing that the soul of the dead transmigrated—i.e., entered the body of a living animal—revered most animals, especially the cow which was believed to contain the soul of the most noble of the departed. The Egyptians considered many of the most common animals sacred, and it is reported that in the time of the Roman occupation of Egypt, the Pharaoh—despite his desire to please the new rulers of his land—could not save a Roman soldier from being stoned to death by an irate mob after the soldier inadvertently killed a cat. The Canaanites, for many years the closest neighbors of the Children of Israel, worshiped gods named the Baalim, which appeared as gigantic bulls or other grotesque forms.

Despite the strict monotheism of the Old Testament, the worship of animals by primitive societies was so widespread a phenomenon that it is not surprising to find traces of it cropping up among the Hebrews in early times. The most famous example of animal worship recorded in the Bible is the story of the Golden Calf. Moses had gone up to the peak of Mount Sinai to receive the Ten Commandments. After many days passed the Israelites began to fear their leader had perished, and their fear led to sacrilege. They persuaded the high priest Aaron to cast their jewelry into a large idol, a calf made of gold. Moses returned to find the "Chosen People" in the midst of pagan ritual, and in anger cast down the two tablets of law he was carrying, shattering them to dust with a loud crash. Destroying the idol, Moses ordered the children of Levi to put to the sword the leaders of the idolatry: "And the children of Levi did according to the word of Moses: and there fell of the people that day about three thousand men" (Exod. 32:28).

The choice of a calf (or bull, as some later translators and commentators maintain) is not unusual. Many ancients revered the bull as a symbol of agricultural productivity. The Egyptian god Apis, with whom the Hebrews were undoubtedly familiar having just been released from their long years of slavery, had the shape of a bull. A major god of Babylonia was a winged bull, and the image of the bull was a central one in Canaanite devotion. Furthermore, in the Bible, God is sometimes addressed as *'abbir Ya'akob*, which means literally "Bull of Jacob." (Many translators, however, use the less discriminatory "Mighty One of Jacob," not wanting to overemphasize the slight taint of paganism in early Judaic theology.) (Gen. 49:24, Isa. 1:24, *et al.*) Bulls and oxen also played a symbolic role in the Temple of Solomon, where horns were placed on top of the altar (I Kings 7:44). The later prophets, Amos, Hosea, and Josiah, all attack the practice: a good sign that it represented a deviation from orthodox monotheism.

One of the most frequently mentioned creatures in the Old Testament is the serpent, which is used alternately as a symbol of evil, as in the story of the temptation of Eve to eat the fatal fruit, and as an object of some reverence. Many early societies, probably the Israelites among them, believed the serpent was immortal, that it renewed its life each time it shed its skin. The Greek god of healing was attended by serpents, and even today the symbol of medicine is a staff intertwined by two snakes. An image very similar to this is the brazen serpent, cast by Moses in the desert of Sinai. The Bible tells how God saw the Israelites losing faith and to punish them sent down "fiery serpents among the people, and they bit the people; and much people of Israel died" (Num. 21:6). Later, seeing the Hebrews had repented, God told Moses to cast a snake of brass and set it upon a pole: ". . . and it shall come to pass, that every one that is bitten, when he looketh upon it, shall live" (Num. 21:8). The Bible later tells how the righteous Hezekiah, when he became king of Judea, ". . . brake in pieces the brazen serpent that Moses had made . . ." (II Kings 18:4), strongly implying that at least some of the Hebrews had begun to worship the statue itself. Some commentators even say that the brass serpent had been worshiped in the early religion of Israel, and only later, when Hebraic monotheism had reached an advanced stage, was the story of the image's miraculous curing powers invented.

There are other indications in the Old Testament that the early Hebrews let some aspects of animal worship enter their religion. The Temple, center of Hebrew spiritual life in the age of the great Judaic kings, is described in the Bible as containing on its inner walls carvings and pictures of ". . . every form of creeping things, and abominable beasts . . ." (Ezek. 8:10). Some commentators believe that the ban on eating the flesh of many animals (see Chapter 4, "Animals—Clean and Unclean," page 20) has its roots in the sacredness of the "unclean" animals. (Swine, for example, were considered holy in ancient Egypt.) However, despite these evidences, it should not be assumed that the Israelites were outright animal worshipers. Animals can be regarded as sacred for many reasons without actually being deified. Images of animals can be used emblematically or symbolically (as indeed they are in Christianity) without being considered literally supernatural. Moreover, the references in the Bible may be isolated and temporary aberrations in the Judaic religious practice may be ignored for they are aberrations that all in time disappeared, leaving no trace. Most, in fact, appear to have been of an origin foreign to the Hebrew nation.

The use of animals in religious ceremonies (as opposed to the actual worship of animals) is referred to quite frequently in the Old Testament, usually taking the form of sacrifices. The first animal sacrifice recorded is the offering made by Abel of the first-born of his flock (Gen. 4:3-5). Ritual sacrifice of an unblemished male goat to atone for a sin is also mentioned in the Bible. Significantly, the laws concerning the purity of animals for sacrifice suggest that the unclean beast was indeed considered unclean, rather than sacred as has been suggested (see above). The Bible describes a later Hebraic ritual in conjunction with the Day of Atonement: a scapegoat is led into the wilderness carrying away with it the sins of the people, and propitiating an evil spirit called Azazel who was believed to dwell in the wilderness (Lev. 16:8, 10, 26).

The New Testament contains no references at all to the worship of animals. However, specific animals, because of their well-known and individualized characteristics, are used emblematically and symbolically. The contrast shown here indicates the origins of animal worship. Originally, an animal and a trait were associated in the minds of the ancients, just as today we apply human characteristics to many animals: the sly fox, the busy bee, the brave lion, the meek lamb. The trait was then probably applied to a person in much the same way that we say someone is "as brave as a lion." The image of Baal as a bull may stem in this way from someone saying of an early Canaanite chieftain, "He's as strong as a bull."

In a monotheistic religion, the process is halted in the early stages, and the animal remains merely a symbol for the deity. In this way, Jesus is often referred to as the Lamb of God, but no special divine significance is attached to every lamb by Christians. The position reached by the Israelites in the system remains unclear. Whether, for example, the brazen serpent remained merely symbolic of God's power or itself became an object of devotion is a subject for scholarly debate. In the New Testament there is no such confusion. The animals mentioned have only limited symbolic significance. The ass stands for peace (thus Jesus rides an ass when he enters his ministry); the dove for innocence; the dog and swine for uncleanliness and vulgarity (yet Christians may eat pork!). Jesus also often used animals in his parables, saying, for example, that you cannot put a camel through a needle's eye.

Animal figures were later used in and about the great medieval cathedrals. Stone gargoyles, representing lambs, dolphins, hens, pelicans, apes, and centaurs adorned the roofs and buttresses of the massive Gothic churches, and while they may have been merely ornamental, a greater significance is indicated by the fact that reformers such as Bernard of Clairvaux felt the need to demand their removal. Drawings of fish, used to symbolize Christ, can be found upon the walls of medieval catacombs.

The image, however, apparently derives wholly from an anagram spelling ICHTHYS (ancient Greek for "fish"), composed of the initial letters of a title in Latinized Greek, which read: "Jesus Christ, God, the Only One, Deliverer."

The Biblical attitude toward the "miracle" is not quite the same as our conception of it—namely, as a suspension or disruption of the laws of Nature. The Biblical writers, as a matter of fact, had no conception of Nature as a realm for which God had instituted laws. Instead, God Himself was thought to preserve His creation, revealing His will in natural events. In this light, the fact of an inexplicable suspension of natural processes becomes more credible.

This interpretation of Nature, on the other hand, does not mean that the Hebrews credited Nature with no regularity. The harmonies they perceived in Nature were understood as revelations of God's fidelity to His covenant. It stands to reason, therefore, that any "miracle" would have to possess some relationship to the sacred bond existing between God and His "Chosen People."

The plagues of Exodus are referred to as "signs and wonders." A sign is understood as the manifest evidence of the presence and activity of God. This notion of signs is applied indiscriminately by the Hebrews to ordinary events such as visits by swarms of locusts, or extraordinary ones such as the death of the first-born in Egypt. To the Hebrew, the miracles were not irrefutable demonstrations of God's existence, but only strong indications. The presence of miracles in the Bible therefore not only did not rule out the necessity of faith and trust in God but, rather, enhanced it.

The reason why there are so many conflicts between science and religion over the question of miracles is that throughout the centuries we have been led to conceive of God as more and more detached from the universe. The Hebrews stressed the immanence of their God, and so the concept of natural law was meaningless to them. Science, in its method, is bound to conceive of the universe as orderly and rational, every event possessing a discernible and understandable cause. The seventeenth-century conception of the universe, thanks to the influence of the fantastic growth of scientific knowledge, was one that embodies a "watchmaker God" who had created a world which would operate once and for all in accord with perfectly comprehensible laws. In unmistakable opposition to the Hebrew notion, the Creator was completely detached from His creation.

Thus, it is easy to see why miracles were so vigorously opposed by scientists in those days. Though there still are remnants of that conflict in existence today, science has since made a more realistic appraisal of its abilities to explain even material phenomena. Its attitude has become less ironclad and more flexible. With the increasing realization by science that problems directly involving nonmaterial factors are outside its scope, the friction between science and religion has been diminishing. Even more important is the realization that it may not necessarily be up to the scientists to decide whether or not an event possesses causes that are other than material.

Fish are focal in two of the miracles of the Bible, both of which are found in the New Testament: "And it came to pass, that, as the people pressed upon him to hear the word of God, he stood by the lake of Gennesaret, And saw two ships standing by the lake: but the fishermen were gone out of them, and were washing *their* nets. And he entered into one of the ships, which was Simon's, and prayed him that he would thrust out a little from the land. And he sat down, and taught the people out of the ship. Now when he had left speaking, he said unto Simon, Launch out into the deep, and let down your nets for a draught. And Simon, answering, said unto him, Master, we have toiled all the night, and have taken nothing: nevertheless at thy word I will let down the net. And when they had this done, they inclosed a great multitude of fishes: and their net brake. And they beckoned unto *their* partners, which were in the other ship, that they should come and help them. And they came, and filled both the ships, so that they began to sink. When Simon Peter saw *it*, he fell down at Jesus' knees, saying, Depart from me; for I am a sinful man, O Lord. For he was astonished, and all that were with him, at the draught of the fishes which they had taken: And so *was* also James and John, the sons of Zebedee, which were partners with Simon. And Jesus said unto Simon, Fear not; from henceforth thou shalt catch men. And when they had brought their ships to land, they forsook all, and followed him" (Luke 5:1–11).

"After these things Jesus shewed himself again to the disciples at the sea of Tiberias; and on this wise shewed he *himself*. There were together Simon Peter, and Thomas called Didymus, and Nathanael of Cana in Galilee, and the *sons* of Zebedee, and two other of his disciples. Simon Peter saith unto them, I go a fishing. They say unto him, We also go with thee. They went forth, and entered into a ship immediately; and that night they caught nothing. But when the morning was now come, Jesus stood on the shore: but the disciples knew not that it was Jesus. Then Jesus saith unto them, Children, have ye any meat? They answered him, No. And he said unto them, Cast the net on the right side of the ship, and ye shall find. They cast therefore, and now they were not able to draw it for the multitude of fishes. Therefore that disciple whom Jesus loved saith unto Peter, It is the Lord. Now when Simon Peter heard that it was the Lord, he girt *his* fisher's coat *unto him*, (for he was naked,) and did cast himself into the sea. And the other disciples came in a little ship; (for they were not far from land, but as it were two hundred cubits,) dragging the net with fishes. As soon then as they were come to land, they saw a fire of coals there, and fish laid thereon, and bread. Jesus saith unto them, Bring of the fish which ye have now caught. Simon Peter went up, and drew the net to land full of great fishes, an hundred and fifty and three: and for all there were so many, yet was not the net broken" (John 21:1-11).

In evaluating these passages we must bear in mind the fact that before the New Testament times the Hebrews knew very little about fishing. This situation is understandable from the geographical situation of the Israelites. Being essentially landlocked, they were not acquainted with the fish of the Mediterranean. The Sea of Galilee, which is the site of most of the fishing referred to in the Gospels, did not become important until New Testament times. The only other important source of fish was the river Jordan.

Fishing was not a sport among the Hebrews, although it was a modest source of food for them in Old Testament times. Three methods of fishing are alluded to in Habakkuk: (1) angling with hook and line (without a rod); (2) use of a small weighted net which was whirled around so that it entered the water in a state of expansion and caught the fish by surprise; (3) use of a dragnet, equipped with floats and weights, so as to permit it to move through the water in a vertical position, bringing the fish either to a boat or to the edge of the water, in a diminishing circle. It is this third method which was most likely used by the Apostles in the miracle of the multitude of fishes.

The passages in Luke and John are sublime illustrations of Christ's singular ability to discover and elicit the profound from the simple. Here, a group of ordinary fishermen (ordinarily sinful, as Peter admits) become transformed by the mysterious selective love of God into immortal crusaders. Since then, the fish has become a profound symbol for the Christians of God's universal love. There is some disagreement as to what exactly was the miracle. It could be that Christ created the multitude of fishes. It could be that the fishes were already present but it took a miraculous knowledge on the part of Christ to reveal it to the fishermen. Be that as it may, it is undeniable that the miracle of fishes was a symbol of a much deeper miracle—the inner transformation which turned a group of fishermen into the future heroes of Christianity, indicated by the significant phrase, "Launch out into the deep." Verse 13 (John 21) is an obvious allusion to the Eucharistic feast. Whether there is any symbolic meaning to the number 153 is difficult to tell. The numbers 1, 5, and 3 were mystical numbers for the Christians.

We find the famous account of the brazen serpent, mentioned above, in Numbers. It goes as follows: "And the people spake against God, and against Moses, Wherefore have ye brought us up out of Egypt to die in the wilderness? for *there is* no bread, neither *is there any* water; and our soul loatheth this light bread. And the Lord sent fiery serpents among the people, and they bit the people; and much people of Israel died. Therefore the people came to Moses, and said, We have sinned, for we have spoken against the Lord, and against thee; pray unto the Lord, that he take away the serpents from us. And Moses prayed for the people. And the Lord said unto Moses, Make thee a fiery serpent, and set it upon a pole: and it shall come to pass, that every one that is bitten, when he looketh upon it, shall live. And Moses made a serpent of brass, and put it upon a pole, and it came to pass, that if a serpent had bitten any man, when he beheld the serpent of brass, he lived" (Num. 21:5–9).

The concern of the Hebrew God over His people was so intense that He proceeded to discipline them by these rigorous means. The devotion to the brazen serpent was not merely confined to the Hebrews. The practice of making an image of an affliction or pest and presenting the image to the deity to have it banished was widespread among the contemporary peoples of the Near East.

There are many who interpret the brazen serpent as a type of pre-figuration of Christ's death on the cross. In this case, the affliction is man's sin. Christ identifies himself with sin in the sense that he willingly bears the load of all the sins of humanity, and offers himself up to God. Anyone, therefore, who wants to rid himself of sin would have to meditate upon the Redemption with faith, and he would be cured.

From the time of Moses on, the Hebrews regarded the brazen serpent as the symbol of the healing power of God. When afflicted with disease, they would burn incense before it in the hope of being relieved. Serpent worship was not unknown to peoples of antiquity, especially in the Near East. This practice dates back to the ancient Egyptians, who paid reverence to serpents as being sacred to their god Ammon. Greeks and Romans were known to worship the healing power of Aesculapius under the figure of a serpent. The expression "fiery serpents" (Hebrew = *seraphim*) in verse 6 (Num. 21) can connote either the brilliant appearance of the animals or the intense pain caused by their bites. It is a fact of herpetology that a great number of poisonous snakes possess brilliant colors, which usually serve as a means of warning to other animals. The "fiery serpents" are found abundantly in arid places, particularly near gulf shores.

In the seventh chapter of Exodus we find another appearance of a snake: "And the Lord spake unto Moses and unto Aaron, saying, When Pharaoh shall speak unto you, saying, Shew a miracle for you: then thou shalt say unto Aaron, Take thy rod, and cast *it* before Pharaoh, *and* it shall become a serpent. And Moses and Aaron went in unto Pharaoh, and they did so as the Lord had commanded: and Aaron cast down his rod before Pharaoh, and before his servants, and it became a serpent. Then Pharaoh also called the wise men and the sorcerers: now the magicians of Egypt, they also did in like manner with their enchantments. For they cast down every man his rod, and they became serpents: but Aaron's rod swallowed up their rods. And he hardened Pharaoh's heart, that he hearkened not unto them; as the Lord had said" (Exod. 7:8–13).

Among the nations of the Near East the rod was a symbol of power and intimacy with God. Thus, Aaron and Moses used it to convince the Egyptians of their mission from on high. As the Scripture reveals, nothing in magical arts was comparable to this phenomenon. It is noteworthy how, in Exodus, the continual contrast is made between the dynamism and vitality of the Hebrew religion and the inefficacy and sterility of the Egyptian religion. The miracle of Aaron's rod is merely one of a number of such illustrations. The serpent held a certain significance for the Egyptians. In art it was sometimes used to symbolize the power and craftiness of the Pharaoh. It is not clear what particular snake is being referred to in this miracle.

Another famous miracle involving a serpent is found in the Acts of the Apostles. St. Paul was performing missionary work on Melita (Malta), an island in the Mediterranean about 80 miles south of Sicily: "And when Paul had gathered a bundle of sticks, and laid *them* on the fire, there came a viper out of the heat, and fastened on his hand. And when the barbarians saw the *venomous* beast hang on his hand, they said among themselves, No doubt this man is a murderer, whom though he hath escaped the sea, yet vengeance suffereth not to live. And he shook off the beast into the fire, and felt no harm. Howbeit, they looked when he should have swollen, or fallen down dead suddenly: but after they had looked a great while, and saw no harm come to him, they changed their minds, and said that he was a god" (Acts 28:3–6).

The natives were not far from right because Paul was to heal a dying man a few days later. (They are referred to as barbarians because they spoke no Greek.) The people of Melita, like the Hebrews, believed serpents to be the agents of God's vengeance. The event emphasizes Paul's implicit trust in God. This miracle was one among scores of miracles and exorcisms which helped to foster the spread of the early Christian Church.

Chapter 4

Animals—Clean and Unclean

No distinction is made, in the Biblical story of Creation, between "clean" animals and "unclean" animals, or between holy animals and unholy. Genesis reads: "And God made the beast of the earth after his kind, and cattle after their kind, and every thing that creepeth upon the earth after his kind: and God saw that *it was* good" (Gen. 1:25).

And although man is given dominion over the animals, the Bible specifies that man's food shall be: ". . . every herb bearing seed, which *is* upon the face of all the earth, and every tree, in the which *is* the fruit of a tree yielding seed . . ." (Gen. 1:29).

Biblical scholars believe the early Hebrews ate meat only on rare occasions, usually ceremonial, and their diet consisted for the most part of bread and milk. Noah and his family were the first to be permitted to eat animal flesh because bread could not be obtained on the ark. It is in the story of Noah that animals are first called clean and unclean: "Of every clean beast thou shalt take to thee by sevens, the male and his female; and of beasts that *are* not clean by two, the male and his female" (Gen. 7:2).

But, even here, the reference is to the animals' fitness as a burnt offering rather than to their food value. The concept of the "clean" animal develops first in reference to sacrificial rites and only later becomes part of dietary law. Thus we find that animals with broken bones are considered unfit as food because, earlier, such an animal was not a suitable sacrifice.

A highly detailed system of dietary laws is given to Moses for the Israelites in the Old Testament books of Leviticus and Deuteronomy. First the clean beast (meaning mammal) is defined: "Whatsoever parteth the hoof, and is clovenfooted, *and* cheweth the cud among the beasts, that shall ye eat" (Lev. 11:3). The passage eliminated from the Israelites' diet many animals then commonly used as food in the Near East, including the camel and the rabbit (unhooved creatures), and swine (which do not chew their cud). Because neighboring tribes ate the flesh of these creatures, the Bible specifically labels them unclean. The prohibition also covers all members of the cat family (including the large felines, sometimes consumed by Semitic nomads), and canines. Dogs, which in ancient times were the scavengers of the towns and villages, were considered ". . . abomination unto the Lord thy God" (Deut. 23:18). Another section of the Scripture catalogues clean mammals: "These *are* the beasts

20

which ye shall eat: the ox [meaning bulls and cows], the sheep, and the goat [all of which were used for sacrifices], The hart, and the roebuck, and the fallow deer, and the wild goat, and the pygarg, and the wild ox, and the chamois" (Deut. 14:4–5). (It is interesting to note the extensive grasp of zoology necessary to properly place these animals in the permitted group.)

Of all the unclean animals, the swine is singled out for special loathing. Rabbinic law, which develops and extends Biblical law, strictly forbids the eating, raising, or keeping of swine. Among the Israelites the swineherd was subject to contempt and abuse, barred by custom from the temple by law and from marriage with any but his own kind. Even in the New Testament story of the Prodigal Son, the swineherd is the symbol of complete human degradation, craving even to eat the food of the pig (Luke 15:15–16). And Jesus cautions his followers not to ". . . cast ye your pearls before swine . . ." (Matt. 7:6). The Biblical injunction against pork is on firm ground, for, especially in the warm climate of the Holy Land, the meat of the pig was apt to cause various diseases. Trichinosis, for example, is a malady produced by worms hatched in the flesh of swine.

The classification of creatures extends to the sea, marking as unclean ". . . all that have not fins and scales in the seas, and in the rivers, of all that move in the waters, and of any living thing which *is* in the waters . . ." (Lev. 11:10), and barring the use of eels, crabs, shrimp, lobsters, and clams as food. Most species of fish which, because of their great abundance in the Mediterranean and the Sea of Galilee, were dietary staples for the Israelites, are, however, considered clean and edible.

The Bible then lists 21 types of flesh-eating birds, including the vulture, the raven, the hawk, the owl, the pelican, and the bat (which, of course, is a mammal), which are unclean and must be held "in detestation."

Unclean animals could never under any circumstances, and despite all forms of consecration, become clean. On the other hand, animals considered clean could become unclean in many different ways. A beast was unfit for food if it died a natural death; if it was attacked and torn by a beast or bird of prey; if it was missing an organ (such as the kidney); if it had a double organ (two livers); if it had fallen and sustained internal injuries; if it had broken bones; if it had missing or dislocated limbs; or, if it was slaughtered in any but the prescribed way.

Although the Bible contains no definite mode of slaughter, the ancient priests formulated a ritual of slaughter which was later codified in Rabbinic law and is still practiced by Orthodox Jews today. The Bible forbids the eating of the blood of any animal. It is believed that the Israelites ascribed to the blood possession of the animal's "soul" or "spirit" (the Hebrew term is more vague than modern English translations); making the blood tabu or forbidden. This explains why all carnivorous animals are considered unclean and why Hebraic law prescribes special cooking of meat to insure that all the blood is removed before it is eaten. Another theory holds that the blood (and "fat," by which is meant the kidneys and the membranes of the liver and intestines as well as fat in the modern sense) belongs to God and therefore may not be consumed by men. The Bible also forbids the cooking of a kid in its mother's milk, and, by extension, the eating of meat with milk or milk products such as cheese and butter. This stems from an old superstition which says that the contact, in the stomach of a man, of meat and milk will cause his domestic stock to stop producing milk.

While the priesthoods of most ancient societies obeyed similar dietary laws, and many ancient writings distinguish between clean and unclean animals, the Israelites are distinct in having food prohibitions that apply to the entire people. While some of the rules derive from considerations of health and sanitation, others seem more arbitrary. According to the Bible, the food restrictions need have no reason apparent to man, for they are the law of God, given to the Israelites to set them apart and above their neighbors. By making the usual restrictions apply to the entire people, the Hebrews became in a sense a nation of priests as befits their self-appellation: "The Chosen People."

Later Biblical commentators have offered other explanations for the dietary laws. Some say that the Hebrews believed unclean animals were inhabited by evil powers and that the eating of their flesh would cause the evil power to enter the man. Others theorize that unclean animals originally were considered sacred and for that reason not fit food. (The pig was considered holy in Egypt. In the Hindu religion, the cow is still sacred today, and its flesh may not be eaten.) The sound sanitary and psychological reasons for assigning most animals to an unclean category cast doubt upon the latter theory.

There are in the New Testament no similar dietary restrictions. The Christian believes he may eat any flesh, pointing to a passage which says: "There is nothing from without a man that, entering into him, can defile him: but the things which come out of him, those are they that defile the man" (Mark 7:15). Thus, a major difference between modern Jewish and Christian practice developed.

The body of Hebraic law regarding animals can be divided, generally speaking, into three categories: those concerning the suitability of specific animals for food; those dealing with the treatment and protection of animals; and those referring more specifically to the use of animals as property.

Of the three, the last is the least important to us, but in Biblical times,

when animals were the major source of property, it had great significance. In the Bible can be found, for example, legislation dealing with
damage done by grazing animals to crops, or with injuries caused by
maddened oxen (Exod. 21:28). Another law requires the digger of an
open pit to pay the owner of any animal that wanders into it, ". . . and
the dead *beast* shall be his" (Exod. 21:34). If an ox gored to death
another ox, the live ox was, by law, sold, and the money divided with
the owner of the dead ox (Exod. 21:35). References can be found to an
Israelite law requiring shepherds to replace missing stock unless they can
prove the loss was no fault of their own.

The Biblical decree against plowing with an ox and an ass together,
while possibly grounded in the general humane attitudes governing other
Biblical laws (in this case, the uneven steps of the two species would
cause suffering to both), may also stem from the principle of avoiding
conjunction of different species, the same principle that forbids crossbreeding and extends even to the use of linen and wool together in the
same garment.

The most significant and eternal Biblical statutes regarding animals
are concerned with their protection and treatment. Generally, the Bible
cautions mankind to remember always that animals are living creatures
of God, and, while not on the same level as man, who was created in
God's image, still higher than the vegetable, or the mere inanimate. God
created animals to serve man (Gen. 1:28), but at the same time placed
upon him the responsibility of treating the animals with kindness and
consideration of their needs. Of course, using animals for food will
cause them pain, but, significantly, the Hebraic laws of slaughter are
designed to be as painless to the victim as possible, even prescribing the
kind of knife and cautioning that the knife must be extremely sharp. The
Hebraic ritualistic slaughter may be the least painful ever devised.

Furthermore, the Bible strongly suggests that man was intended to be
a vegetarian (Gen. 1:29), and that only in the time of the Deluge, when
the eating of animals became a necessity for survival, was Noah permitted to use animals for food, and then, of course, only when following
strict rules. That the Ten Commandments decree a Sabbath, or day of
rest for beasts as well as men (Exod. 20:10), vividly portrays the Biblical
attitude toward living things.

Examples of Biblical kindness to animals abound. Isaac discovers that
Rebekah would be a proper wife for him when she remembers to bring
water for his camels as well as himself (Gen. 24:14–15). The Bible also
tells how Moses, after driving off the shepherds who had refused to let
the seven daughters of Micah use a well, helped the girls water the
flock (Exod. 2:17). And Nathan tells David a parable suggesting that in
the age of the great Judaic kings, lambs were often kept as household

pets: "But the poor *man* had nothing, save one little ewe lamb, which he had bought and nourished up; and it grew up together with him, and with his children; it did eat of his own meat, and drank of his own cup, and lay in his bosom, and was unto him as a daughter" (II Sam. 12:3).

When God speaks out of the Whirlwind to Job, rebuking him for questioning the Divine Judgment, He shows extreme understanding and consideration for animals (Job 39). David, one of the greatest of the Children of Israel, is noted for his gentleness toward his flock.

Biblical law specifies that the ox may not be muzzled when threshing grain, a practice probably common among the neighbors of the early Hebrews (Deut. 25:4). The Bible also considers the feelings of the animal as parent, forbidding the slaughtering of a young animal in the first seven days of its life (Lev. 22:27), and barring the removal of any bird from its eggs (Deut. 22:6). Another law bans the slaughter of an animal and its offspring on the same day.

Kindness to animals is reflected in the suggestion that a passerby, seeing an animal struggle beneath too heavy a burden, must interrupt his journey to unload the beast, even if it might belong to an enemy (Exod. 23:5). According to Mosaic law, the first-born of animals is as sacred to God as the first-born to man.

This attitude extends into other realms. Hunting as a sport was always looked upon with disfavor by the Hebrews. Esau was generally condemned by the Hebrews because of his fondness for hunting, and later writers regarded hunting as surrender to the baser instincts. The authors of the Talmud, a book of law written to amplify and explain the Bible, carries kindness to animals to the extreme, saying that the beast of burden should be fed before its owner. It also forbids buying animals unless suitable food is on hand to feed them.

Medieval rabbis continually specified a man's duty to feed and shelter homeless animals, and strongly condemned all types of cruelty, including overloading oxen and tormenting household or city animals such as dogs and cats, despised as they were. Even the spurring of horses was criticized! Judah Hanasi, a rabbi of the Middle Ages, is reputed to have suffered from a toothache for 13 years for allowing a calf to be led to slaughter, but the pain is alleged to have ceased abruptly when he saved a litter of kittens from death.

In general, the rabbis taught that he who hurt animals hurt his own soul. This attitude is also shown in the fact that the usual blessing said by Orthodox Jews upon putting on new clothing is omitted if the garment is made of fur or leather, since an animal died to make the garment. Christian doctrine, while it does not put the same emphasis on kindness to animals, is basically sympathetic to the Old Testament attitude, basing the belief on a passage from the Book of Proverbs: "A righteous *man* regardeth the life of his beast: but the tender mercies of the wicked *are* cruel" (Prov. 12:10).

Although kindness to animals is based upon the sanctity of all life, the question of the existence of an animal's soul has been debated by Bible experts without being satisfactorily resolved. The Bible in several places (notably Lev. 17:11 and Eccles. 3:19–21) seems to suggest that animals *do* have souls, but nowhere in either the Old or New Testaments is any reference made to the reward or punishment of any animal after death.

The Old Testament in particular seems to suggest that animals were morally and legally responsible for their actions, capable of good and bad deeds, and of knowing right from wrong. In the Book of Jonah (Chapter 3) we learn that even the animals were required to take part in the fast of Nineveh. Another interesting example pointing to the likelihood of trials for animals can be found in Exodus: "If an ox gore a man or a woman, that they die; then the ox shall be surely stoned, and his flesh shall not be eaten . . ." (Exod. 21:28).

Chapter 5
Symbolism of the Bible

"All these things spake Jesus unto the multitude in parables; and without a parable spake he not unto them; That it might be fulfilled which was spoken by the prophet, saying, I will open my mouth in parables; I will utter things which have been kept secret from the foundation of the world" (Matt. 13:34–35).

The parable occurs frequently throughout both the Old and the New Testaments and also related Semitic literature. It is found in all folk literature. To appreciate the significance of the parable, it is necessary to be acquainted with the nature of symbolism as employed by the ancient Semitic peoples.

Symbolism and allegory appear in the narrative of creation; in most of the events of Hebrew history; in the sayings of the Prophets; and in the Psalms, the Proverbs, and especially Revelations. The allegories and parables of the Bible are presented in a form much resembling the pattern of a dream. Dreams, it must be remembered, were regarded by the Biblical authors as a medium of divine communication. Consequently we find in the parables the use of condensation of images and a preponderance of seemingly illogical use of symbols. Often a certain object is represented in the same passage by more than one symbol, a technique which makes it difficult for us to interpret some of the parables. The parable truly succeeds in endowing simple and ordinary situations with profound implications.

The Hebrew predilection for this kind of figurative expression is indicative of the mystical attitude which has also dominated much of Oriental philosophy and religion. The mystical mind is able to confront an ordinary phenomenon and perceive the divine at work in it. Each little event becomes, as it were, the turning point of the cosmos. The boundary is blurred between the material and the nonmaterial, between the dream and the reality.

The God of the Old Testament permeates the world He has created with a degree of intimacy unimaginable to the contemporary Western mind. This is why it is so difficult for us to grasp the full meaning of the figurative language of the Old Testament. In order to be fully appreciated, the parables should not be explained, but rather experienced; to gain the total mystical effect of the Bible, we must dream along with its authors.

Consider Ezekiel's Parable of the Eagles: "And say, Thus saith the Lord God, A great eagle with great wings, longwinged, full of feathers,

26

which had divers colours, came unto Lebanon, and took the highest branch of the cedar: He cropped off the top of his young twigs, and carried it into a land of traffic: he set it in a city of merchants. He took also of the seed of the land, and planted it in a fruitful field; he placed *it* by great waters, *and* set it *as* a willow tree. And it grew, and became a spreading vine of low stature, whose branches turned toward him, and the roots thereof were under him: so it became a vine, and brought forth branches, and shot forth sprigs. There was also another great eagle with great wings and many feathers; and, behold, this vine did bend her roots toward him, and shot forth her branches toward him, that he might water it by the furrows of her plantation. It was planted in a good soil by great waters, that it might bring forth branches, and that it might bear fruit, that it might be a goodly vine. Say thou, Thus saith the Lord God, Shall it prosper? shall he not pull up the roots thereof, and cut off the fruit thereof, that it wither? it shall wither in all the leaves of her spring, even without great power, or many people to pluck it up by the roots thereof. Yea, behold, *being* planted, shall it prosper? shall it not utterly wither, when the east wind toucheth it? it shall wither in the furrows where it grew" (Ezek. 17:3–10).

The type of eagle to which this parable refers is most probably the "Golden Eagle," technically known as *Aquila chrysaëtos*. This bird is found throughout Eurasia, in North Africa, and in North America. It primarily inhabits mountainous regions, but is also found in some lowland forested areas. The adult of the Palestinian form is dark brown, with the back of the head and nape of the neck golden, and the tail usually speckled with gray. Its legs are feathered down to the feet. The male measures in length up to 35 inches, has a wingspread of up to 84 inches, and a tail up to 15 inches long. The female is somewhat larger, up to 41 inches in length, 92 inches in wingspread, and a tail up to 16 inches long. This eagle feeds on hares, rabbits, marmots, fawns, lambs, grouse, and waterfowl, as well as upon other large birds. Its nest is a large structure of sticks built on the ledge of a cliff. It breeds once a year, and lays two or three eggs.

In order to appreciate the significance of the eagle in Hebrew culture as revealed in Ezekiel's parable, it will be necessary to discuss it in the total context of the parable. It is in this parable that Ezekiel prophesies the capture of Jerusalem at the hands of the Babylonians, a prophecy which became historical fact in 586 B.C. The imagery employed by the prophet was hardly unfamiliar to his people. The bird had always been a source of singular fascination to the Hebrew mind. Apparently it was suggestive of the mysterious, and of the transcendental.

When discussing the imagery of the Old Testament we must bear in mind the Hebrew predilection for using concrete things as a basis for conceptualization and communication. For this reason, much of the Old Testament abounds with parables and allegories. It often becomes difficult, as we shall see later, to distinguish what is figuratively intended from what is literally true.

In the story of the creation, the Spirit of God is described, in the original Hebrew, as *hovering* upon the face of the waters. The hagiographer uses the verb *rachaph*, which in a later book of the Bible is used to describe a parent eagle fluttering over its young. The word for eagle was *nesher*, which sounds quite similar to *nephesh*, the ancient Hebrew word which stood for the spirits which were believed to animate the phenomena of nature. To the Hebrew the great eagle, soaring swiftly among the mountain heights, was a symbol of power as well as of protection.

Besides the familiarity of his audience with the imagery of the eagle, the bird was an especially appropriate symbol for Ezekiel from the standpoint of his own religious attitudes. The prophet placed high emphasis on the divine attributes of holiness and power. In this particular parable, however, the eagle is used to describe the enemies of God, or more appropriately, the enemies of the Israelites. It is important to note Ezekiel's belief that God and His "Chosen People" were indivisible. This quasi-Oriental attitude toward social religion is grasped only with difficulty by the Western mind. Ezekiel, ironically enough, is usually regarded as the great contributor of individualism to the development of religious thought. He constantly accuses Israel of profaning the holiness of its union with God. The capture of Israel by the Babylonians constitutes a just retribution.

The eagle is used to symbolize the "anti-God," to be identified with the Babylonians, as individualized in Nebuchadnezzar, their king. Nebuchadnezzar, like all Babylonian rulers, wore a regalia of eagle wings.

The eagle is described as having divers colors (Ezek. 17:3). This is a clear reference to the gaudily colored representations of the eagle as a symbol of royalty found on Babylonian monuments.

The cedar of Lebanon constituted a vivid and nostalgic piece of imagery to the contemporary Jew. This plant contributed a great deal of beauty to the Israel countryside, and came to be a symbol of the majesty, endurance, and fertility of the Jewish nation. We can imagine the emotional effect upon Ezekiel's audience of an eagle thus molesting a cedar.

The top of the tree refers to King Jechonias and the other princes carried into captivity by the Babylonians. The "seed of the land" (Ezek. 17:5) refers to Sedecias whom Nebuchadnezzar appointed king of the exiled Jews. The second eagle mentioned in verse 7 (Ezek. 17) symbolizes Egypt. The vine which developed from the seed of Sedecias "bends her roots" toward this eagle, indicating the collusion between Sedecias' followers and the Egyptians, which was to come to naught.

And the Jewish nation *did* survive. God would allow his people to be purged but not to be destroyed.

The imagery of the eagle is used in a number of places throughout the Old Testament. The sight of an eagle soaring over the heads of the weary Israelites during their exodus filled them with a feeling of exhilaration and encouragement. In the poetry of the words, "I bare you on eagles' wings," Israel recognized her experience of God.

In these manifestations of bird imagery, we can perceive the full Hebrew religious experience. The Egyptians, too, represented their primary god, Ra, by means of a bird. It is not certain whether the Egyptians influenced the Hebrews in this regard. The refinement of Hebrew theistic notions in comparison to those of the Egyptian is, on the other hand, indisputable. The Jews allowed their one and only God to possess much more transcendence than the Egyptians bestowed on their gods, or even on their supreme power, *Amen*.

The problem of the Westerner in attempting a literary or philosophical approach to Hebraic animal parables revolves around the concept of dichotomy. (In Oriental and Middle-East philosophy, dichotomy is even less revered.) The distinction between symbolism and reality is considerably more blurred than in the philosophical attitudes of the Western world. This disparity of approach can be readily seen by comparing the parable of the eagles to any ordinary Homeric simile.

If we are to appreciate the parables of the Old Testament it is important to understand the extent to which philosophical and religious notions and their respective genres of communication are influenced by culture. It is possible that many of the elements of Old Testament allegories and parables can be traced back to influences from primitive Hebrew notions.

A number of Biblical scholars suggest that primitive man tended to deify the phenomena of Nature with which he was immediately confronted and over which he exerted little or no control. This opinion does not refute the existence of monotheism among the primitive Hebrews; it merely declares that the primitive Hebrew had not yet evolved philosophically to the level of monotheism as we conceive it today. Primitive man was pragmatic rather than speculative. Cause and effect, idea and reality, were simply inconceivable at the time. Because he could not analyze the mysteries of natural phenomena, he venerated them. Many of the rites of the Old Testament were consequently associated with sacred mountains, trees, stones, etc.

Thus arose the Hebrew fondness for parable and allegory, and the corresponding lack of effort to separate the symbol from that which is symbolized.

Chapter 6
Zoology of the Bible

On the Second Day: ". . . God said, Let the earth bring forth grass, the herb yielding seed, *and* the fruit tree yielding fruit after his kind, whose seed *is* in itself, upon the earth: and it was so."

On the Fourth Day: ". . . God created great whales, and every living creature that moveth, which the waters brought forth abundantly, after their kind, and every winged fowl after his kind: and God saw that *it was* good."

On the Fifth Day: ". . . God made the beast of the earth after his kind, and cattle after their kind, and every thing that creepeth upon the earth after his kind: and God saw that *it was* good.

"So God created man in his *own* image, in the image of God created he him; male and female created he them.

"And God blessed them, and God said unto them, Be fruitful, and multiply, and replenish the earth, and subdue it: and have dominion over the fish of the sea, and over the fowl of the air, and over every living thing that moveth upon the earth."

It takes years for a baby to develop an ability to distinguish between the bewildering array of objects with which he is confronted for the first time. At first, he can only tell that "familiar" objects, such as his parents and his cradle, are different from all the "unfamiliar" things with which he comes in increasing contact as he becomes more and more able to move around. He will not be able to remember different strangers who come to the house; will have to be constantly reminded that the big boxlike thing his parents drive is called an "automobile."

Similarly, it must have seemed a bewildering task to primitive man to classify all the animals and plants he found in the world about him. Nevertheless, even the oldest cave paintings show a growing desire to classify animals in groups. Different deer are pictured alike, and domesticated animals are put in different groupings from wild animals. Even at the earliest stages of his history, man recognized differences and similarities between animals.

The Bible represents one of the earliest recorded attempts at a grand scheme of classification. It is one that makes no pretensions of being a scientific analysis because it was originally designed for a primitive pastoral people who could have no conception of exotic animals and plants beyond their immediate lands, and who had yet to develop an appreciation of scientific method. Thus, Biblical classification tries to relate to the needs of the people for which it is intended, which is why it is largely designed to be a framework for a system of dietary laws.

The scheme of Genesis is based on several approaches to classification. First, it considers the origins and habitats of various groups of animals. Fish were created and live in the sea, all the animals that fly are "birds," the "beasts of the earth" are so named because they arose from and live on the earth. Further, other parts of the Bible indicate a classification based on means of reproduction. All animals whose means of reproduction escaped the early Israelites (just as they escaped scientists until the eighteenth century) are classified as "fast breeding." These include the insects and reptiles, and are differentiated from higher four-legged animals, whose means of reproduction was understood. More important, animals are ordered according to their practical usefulness to man, so that domesticated animals are distinguished from their wild relatives. Thus the Bible divides the animal kingdom into four main groupings: the *Behemoth*,* which includes all domesticated and wild, higher four-legged animals; *Fowl*, including all flying forms such as birds, bats, flying insects, etc.; the *Swimmers*, being all the fish but not including the whales (see page 131), a distinction which has been verified by modern taxonomy; and the *Reptiles*, the animals which creep on the earth.

The Bible is unique in connecting this system of classification to an evolution of life, placing the appearance of these animal types in some sort of chronological order. Christianity rests firmly on the idea of Creation, which means there was a beginning and will be an end to life as we know it. The concept of passage of time and of a history of life is very important because it helps to explain the strange world of diverse animals and plants by relating them to man. Their origins and man's lie in the common creative act of God, a friendly force that gave man dominion over the rest of life.

Considering our current, much more detailed knowledge of evolution, Genesis is remarkably close in some respects. It states that life first arose in the waters and then penetrated the land, a fact mirrored in our modern hypothesis that such animals as the lungfish, salamander, and lizards represent transitional phases between the fish and higher forms such as the mammals. It further seems to indicate that plants and animals invaded the earth at different times, which certainly seems true in the light of modern evidence.

What the Bible does not do, however, is state directly any connection between different groups of animals which arose at different times. This is because God created each group separately. Thus, it does not attempt to consider the evolutionary implications of classification but

* As opposed to "*A* Behemoth." See page 97.

rather how God made each animal especially suited to its environment, a proof of the logic of His order in a seemingly chaotic world. Thus, it makes the mistake of lumping birds and bats together because both have wings and fly. Later studies of the detailed bone structure of the "wings" of bats and birds have shown that they are really quite different and that, surprisingly enough, bats are more closely related to horses and lions than eagles or roosters.

In our modern system of classification, we still use this approach of studying how animals are adapted to their environment although, of course, a more limited, systematic approach is used. The world affords animal and plant life an infinitude of environments into which they can fit, adapt to, and live in. Certain bacteria can be found even in the hottest geysers, the crustacean *Artemia* can live in the saltiest rock deposits, and some parasites spend almost their whole lives in the intestines of sheep and cows. The modern biological science of ecology studies how populations of animals and plants are fitted and related to their environments. It studies how animals are suited to move from one environment to another: for example, wind disperses seeds, ocean currents carry algae populations thousands of miles, birds undergo seasonal migrations, and herds of horses once migrated over half the earth. It then studies what it is about a particular environment that will tend to isolate one group of animals from another. Two groups of Danish viola are so classified because one will grow only on chalky (alkaline) soil, the other only on acid soil; the lemurs of Madagascar are separated from the rest of the world by the water around the island on which they live, and so on. Finally, it studies what changes these different environments have wrought on the animal and plant itself; plants that thrive in the mountains of California are normally smaller than those of the valleys; cave animals are often characterized by degenerate and nonfunctional eyes, and so on.

On the basis of considerations like these we are able to define the fundamental unit of classification, the *species*. A species of animal or plant is a group of populations which have become so isolated and different from related forms that they are no longer able to interbreed with them. They may have become so different that their reproductive organs will be physically incapable of interbreeding; while hybrids that are conceived may be infertile or inviable, etc.

By defining certain environments, such as the sea, the desert, and the cave, much as the Bible tried to define the type of habitat in which animals are found, modern ecology carries on the approach to classification of earlier times. It also affords us a valuable insight into the process of evolution still going on today, and its mechanism of action through environmental selection.

Just as the Bible recognized that domesticated animals must be considered separately from wild animals, so modern theories of evolution and classification recognize the value of breeding experiments as a means of observing evolution greatly speeded up. By domesticating over 300 species of plants, as well as 100 kinds of animals, like the horse, dog, and cat, man has often succeeded in pushing evolution to its limits of specialization. This artificial selection has led to an amazing amount of "speciation" within man's history. For example, there are only three species of wild horses left, but there are many breeds of domesticated horses. Man has purposely isolated particular horses to get the fastest ones as racehorses; plants are selected for disease resistance; sheep are selected for heavier coats; and so on.

Cases of fast natural evolution within our own time have also been recorded. One of the most striking cases has been the development of "industrial melanism," or the appearance of dark forms among a number of species of moth. In industrial areas, trees tend to become covered with soot and so these moths are better protected against their enemies because of their dark coloration. Melanic forms were first reported in 1850 from Manchester, England, but today it is quite rare to find any light-colored examples of those particular moths in any part of northern England. It has even been possible to observe evolution greatly speeded up in the laboratory. Demerec has been able to "train" bacteria to be resistant to penicillin by exposing succeeding generations to gradually increasing amounts of it. It is significant that sudden exposure only to a *large* amount will kill them; and this shows that evolution occurs only in small steps over normally long periods of time. (It took millions of years to evolve the gigantic reptilian dinosaurs from smaller ancestors.) Thus, classification can never be absolute, as species are constantly changing and various intergradations will always be found. Also, all "species" of animals appear to be changing in more than one way.

The realization of how and why different species can arise from one common ancestor is but one step to a proper understanding of the totality of evolution. A particular environment can accommodate not one but many species. Thus, they will tend to evolve as groups. Each environment will impose its particular needs on its resident populations, an effect which will be mirrored in their anatomy. All lions are classified as members of one species, but there are other similar animals, such as the tiger and leopard, which have adapted to the same type of existence as animals of prey. They all have long, sharp, retractable claws, sharp teeth, and strong jaws. In order to define the group as a whole, it is necessary to introduce a new unit of classification bigger than the species: the *genus*. The genus distinguishes a group of species on the basis of a similar, unique anatomy. It also indicates that its component species are relatively closely related and probably came from one common ancestral species.*

Various methods have come into particular use in the last few years to determine how closely related two species are. It has been found that if the bloods of relatively unrelated species are mixed, they will "clump." The closer the two species, the less clumping there will be. Another approach has involved a comparison of the embryological developments of two species; distantly related species will have less similar embryologies than closely related ones. This is often also useful in determining the common ancestry of seemingly quite different groups of animals.

The development of classificatory groupings higher than genus, relies to a large extent on another line of evidence, that of fossils. Fossils are remnants of living things from bygone times and are perhaps the most direct evidence for the process of evolution which underlies the order of classification. By tabulating the appearance, anatomy, etc., of various fossils from various times and correlating the findings with geological evidence which indicates what sort of environment they lived in, it is possible to "see" how two groups of animals, originally quite similar, gradually developed differences and became more and more distinct. Thus, the members of the cat tribe can be put into a higher grouping called an *Order,* along with dogs, bears, weasels, hyenas, etc., called the *Carnivora* because they are all flesh eating. These, in turn, can be classified into a still higher grouping, the *Class,* here called *Mammalia.* This contains animals like whales, bats, mice, horses, deer, etc.— all of which suckle their young with milk produced by mammary glands.

Fossil evidence thus puts classification in an over-all historical perspective. Animals that seem quite different today will often be seen to come from similar ancestors. To a large extent, evolution is a process

* In scientific papers, the lion is usually referred to as *Panthera leo,* the first term being its generic and the last its specific name. This system of "binomial nomenclature" was first developed by the Swedish botanist Carl von Linné (Carolus Linnaeus) in his monumental *Systema Naturae,* published in 1758. Linnaeus' ideas on classification were derived from the religious dogma of his time, which in turn was rooted in the Bible. He appreciated the ordering of animals and plants in the Bible as proof of God's logic, feeling that "without classification—only chaos." Working mostly in Sweden, but also collecting in other northern European countries, he was able to list 4235 separate animal species. Today, we know of a million animal and 265,000 plant species, and that there are thousands more yet to be discovered. Linnaeus further realized that species tend to fall into clusters, and so he devised the concept of a hierarchy of classification. Thus species could be organized into increasingly larger groupings, each reflecting more and more directly the unity of God's Creation. He did not, however, consider this hierarchy as reflecting a process of evolutionary diversification, and held each species to be basically static.

of diversification, and the problem of classification becomes harder and harder as time goes by. Professor George Gaylord Simpson estimates that there are probably about 2 million living species of animals, a figure that, while double the usual estimates, still falls far short of some, notably the entomologists', who have stated that we have so far discovered only one tenth of all living insect species. However, given 2 million today, and that the life span of a species ranges between 500,000 to 5,000,000 years, and that the length of time since life began is 1 to 2 billion years, then the total number of species in history probably lies between 50 and 5000 million.

Mammals belong to a still higher grouping, known as the (Class) *Vertebrata*, which includes also the fish, amphibians, birds, and reptiles; all of which have in common a vertebrated backbone. This internal support, along with a nervous system which relies mainly on control by a "brain" has allowed a different line of adaptation to that which led to, for instance, the insects. Insects have an external covering skeleton which limits their size, and a nervous system which relies mainly on reflexes at the nerve endings themselves, causing them to live stereotyped lives in specific environments. There are hundreds of thousands of insect species but only one species of man, because men have developed a flexibility that allows them to live in almost any environment.

As has already been mentioned, the Old Testament was originally written in ancient or classical Hebrew, though there are versions of parts of it in Aramaic. The New Testament, which Jews do not accept, was written in Greek, except for one book which was also written in Aramaic. At a later date, a wholly Greek version, which has unfortunately been lost as a unit, was assembled. A complete Latin version, known as the Vulgate, was translated from this. This became the sole and standard reference Bible for the Christian world of both the Western and the Eastern Roman Empires. The Old Testament remained in the Hebrew language for use by the Jews. When the Western Roman Empire collapsed, the Vulgate was retranslated, and through the centuries it appeared in various authorized forms. Today, the Roman Catholic Church approves the use of translations in a number of Western languages, including English.

In the Eastern (Orthodox Greek and Russian) area, still other Latin versions appeared. The Armenians produced an independent Bible; versions in various languages and scripts were devised for the Coptic Church of Egypt, the Abassian Church of Ethiopia, and numerous sects in Central Asia. Some of these were derived directly from the Hebrew Old Testament; several included other canonical works, such as the Acts of the Apostles.

The first important version of the Bible in the English language is the famous King James Version. Although a Catholic, James the First ordered an English translation to be made for his people, who were by then predominantly Protestant. The result was a work of exquisite literary skill and beauty, one that has lasted with slight changes until today. That the greatest literary work ever compiled should also have been so superbly—if not uniquely—translated into our language is a happy coincidence.

Despite the beauty of the King James Version, it is not perfect. Its exactness, particularly for our purposes, leaves something to be desired. In the first place, the knowledge of Old Hebrew, and even of ancient Greek, and classical Latin possessed by the translators and compilers (it was 1611, let us not forget) was not that of today's philological scholars. Secondly, and more importantly for us, these men knew nothing of zoological science. They had considerable knowledge of the wildlife of Great Britain, but they had only Aristotle and Pliny to rely on for information about the wildlife of the Mediterranean Basin and adjacent lands. They had never seen or even heard of an Aurochs (which had by then been extinct for some centuries), an Addax, or a Bubalis. They knew of hippopotami, crocodiles, and camels, but their concepts of them were vague.

Thus, when they came upon a name of an animal, they tended naturally to take the Latin interpretation of it first—the animals of Italy are closer to those of England than are the animals of Greece. If they were in doubt, they had resort to the Greeks of old; and if they still were not sure of the true meaning, they tried to interpret the nature of the beast as described in Hebrew. Limited in their knowledge, they were forced to choose the closest animal (in size, shape, and behavior) that they knew in their *own* land. The performance they turned in, while quite extraordinary, is not wholly satisfactory.

As soon as the Bible was available in English and other secular languages, scholars set to work studying it, analyzing it, and retranslating it. These commentators and translators were often bad philologists, knew nothing of etymology, and had no concept of semantics. Worst of all, they knew very little about wildlife. This period of confusion lasted until the end of the last century, and in some respects still lingers. Through the machinations of these nonscientific commentators, all manner of complexities in the identification of the animals originally mentioned in the Bible arose.

Modern science has added further confusion. The proper identification and classification of animals (called "systematics or the science of taxonomy as applied to animal life"), though precise, is still undergoing refinement. Moreover, adjustments have had to be made in practically every aspect of classification since Linnaeus founded our modern binomial system. He knew only four and a half thousand kinds of animals; today we know between 1 and 2 million. In his day, little was known of nine tenths of the earth's surface, outside of Europe. Therefore, even if the translators who prepared the King James Version named the animal properly, and the nineteenth-century commentators did not change their decision, modern systematic zoology may have altered its Latin or scientific name several times in the past hundred years.

As was mentioned briefly in the Introduction, these matters raise very real problems. To solve them we have adopted the following plan. First, our list of the animals (see pages 87, 135, 173, and 181) was compiled from the King James Version, though old English titles—such as "glede" for kite and "ossifrage" for the osprey—have been converted to their current names. The resulting list proved to be fairly short and simple. There are fewer than 100 "kinds" of animals mentioned in the Bible. These kinds varied from individual *species* to *families* and even—in cases such as "frogs," "fish," and "songbirds"—to much larger associations. All but a few on the list appear to be named correctly. Less than 5 per cent are really obscure.

Armed with this list, we can take each of these kinds of animals in turn and discuss just what they must be, what they might be, and what the various commentators and translators have said they thought they were, and thus track each one down. This entails, first, going back to the ancient Hebrew name for the animal and ascertaining what Hebrew philologists say the animal was and, second, investigating those names which are recorded only in the Greek or Latin originals. The Greeks were no better translators of Hebrew than were the seventeenth-century English scholars, and there are several animals mentioned in the New Testament that do not appear in the Old Testament. What is more, the Latin version is of little help because it occasionally misinterpreted the Greek. A striking example is the confusion on the part of the Romans concerning the animal named by the Greeks *ailuros*. They called or translated this as *felis*, or "Cat," when it actually referred to the Polecat or Ferret (*Putorius putorius*), which the Greeks had domesticated to keep down mice. When they finally obtained *real* cats from Egypt, they at first called them "Egyptian Weasels." These "weasels" were actually Genets (*Genetta*), which the Egyptians, the Sicilians, and the Corsicans had long before domesticated. They were not weasels at all, but Civets!

When all the confusions and complications have been put on record, we can sum each up and suggest just which animal may *really* have been originally referred to. These suggestions are not intended to be in any way definitive or authoritative but are founded solely on current published knowledge of just what animals live in the Bible lands today, and which are positively known to have lived there when the Bible was being written. Luckily the list of fauna is not great and does not contain large numbers of closely related kinds of animals. In fact, the majority of the animals so listed are represented by but a single species. This naturally makes our task both easier and less susceptible to error. Then, too, we always have the original Hebrew philology and the findings of experts in that field. The Ancient Hebrews were consummate naturalists; they loved their animals; and their language is astonishingly precise from a semantic point of view.

PHOTO CREDITS

On the following pages are photographs of animals in the Bible. Most of them were taken by the author in the Holy Land. Others were obtained by him through the efforts and cooperation of individuals, photographers, and institutions throughout the world. The author wishes to credit the following and thank them for their help in the difficult task of rounding up the animals of the Bible:

The Sperm Whale, from Ivan T. Sanderson's *Follow the Whale;* Red Deer, Fallow Deer, Wolf, Fox, Weasel, Badger, Mole-Rat, Elephant, Ostrich, Heron, Lammergeier, Quail, Crane, Lapwing, Scorpion: *Zoological Society of London*. The Aurochs, Bubal, Falcon, Lizard, Skink, Carp, Fly, Leech: *Courtesy, American Museum of Natural History*. The Addax, Bat, Mouse, Kite, Osprey, Peacock: *New York Zoological Society*. Lion: *SATour*. Baboon: *Chris Pisart*. Bittern: *Simon de Waard*. Swan: *Rudolph E. Leppert, Jr.* Cuckoo, Swallow: *Georg Schutzenhofer*. Cobra, Frog, Hornet, Clothes Moth: *Walter Jarchow*. Mosquito: *Walther Rohdich*. Spider: *Harald Doering*. Sparrow: *François Merlet*. Flea, Louse: *M. B. Mittleman*. Frank W. Lane of London was especially helpful in tracking down many of these photographs.

1. Horses were regarded as war "machines" rather than draft or riding vehicles by the Ancient Hebrews.

2. The mule was held in high esteem as a work animal.

3. Asses, or donkeys, and especially white ones, were the steeds of both important persons and the peasants.

3. The Wild Ass of Asia is called the Onager. Now rare, it was once hunted and possibly tamed throughout the Near East.

4. Wild Boars are still found in limited numbers in a few wild parts of Palestine. They were plentiful in Biblical times.

5. The Domestic Pig was "an abomination unto the Lord;" yet swine were kept by the Israelites of old.

6. Hippopotamuses were not found in Palestine in Biblical times, but the Hebrews knew them from Egypt.

7. Above all other animals, the camel dominates the countries of the Near East today as it did in ancient times. There have always been many distinct breeds developed for different purposes.

8. The Red Deer (*Cervus elephas*) is the Eurasian representative of our Wapiti or Elk. It was always the principal object and symbol of the hunt in Europe and the Near East.

9. Fallow Deer appear to be indigenous to the Mediterranean area, whence they were transported to western Europe as park animals.

10. The Aurochs was one of the species of Wild Cattle left in western Eurasia after the last retreat of the ice. It was probably the ancestor of most of our domestic breeds.

11. A picture of cattle today. The exact breeds of ancient times and their appearance are not known.

12. The Bubal Hartebeest (*Alcelaphus buselaphus*) was once common across North Africa and possibly in Palestine. It is now thought to be extinct, the last one having died in Paris in 1923.

13. The Addax, a screw-horned Horse-Antelope, is a rare denizen of the Sahara and probably occurred in northern Arabia in ancient times.

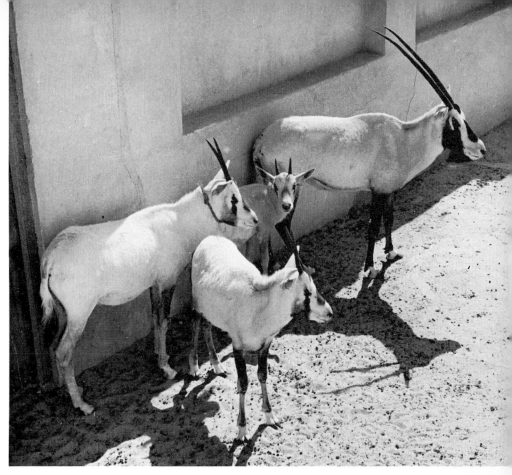

14. The Arabian Oryx, one of the rapier-horned Horse-Antelopes, is now verging on extinction in southern Arabia, but once apparently ranged as far north as Lebanon.

15. This delicate little antelope is still found in western and southern Arabia. Gazelles appear to have been well known to the Hebrews.

16. Domestic sheep were perhaps the early Hebrews' most valuable possessions. Their ancestors in Mesopotamia were basically sheep herders and these animals held a prominent place in their symbolism.

17. The Aoudad, also called Maned or Barbary Sheep, are magnificent inhabitants of the North African mountains and were apparently indigenous to Mt. Sinai and even parts of Palestine in ancient times.

18. There are several distinct types or species of ibexes, a form of wild goat, distributed from the Alps to Ethiopia and southern Arabia.

19. Domestic Goats were well known to the inhabitants of the Near East from prehistoric times. They have probably done more to destroy the vegetational cover of these countries than even man himself.

20. There were lions in Palestine, and even in Greece, in Biblical times, but they are now confined to Africa and a small pocket in what is now Pakistan.

21. Leopards are still found in some remote mountainous districts of the Near East, and even in the Caucasus. They were ever marauders of domestic animals.

22. The Ancient Hebrews had a loathing for the domestic cat that almost exceeds reason. This is probably due to their being sacred animals in the abominated temples of both Egypt and Assyria.

23. The original "bear" of western literature is the Brown Bear (*Ursus*) of Eurasia, of which one species is indigenous to the lands of the Bible. They are related to our Grizzlies.

24. Whether wolves still exist in the Levant is a moot point but in Biblical times they were fairly common. Apart from the Indian Wolf and the little Coyote, all are of one species, though they vary in size and color, like dogs.

25. One of the most interesting creatures of the Near and Middle East is the so-called Pariah Dog. They were "an abomination" to the Hebrews, but it is now believed that they constitute a true breed if not subspecies of the dog tribe.

26. Jackals are the little wild lurchers of the Bible Lands. They are useful scavengers and still very numerous.

27. There is a representative of our common Red Fox in Palestine and it was well known to the early Hebrews.

28. The Striped Hyaena (*Hyaena hyaena*) is still not uncommon in Palestine and adjacent areas. It is a nocturnal scavenger and can be dangerous, but it also is easily tamed.

29. There are a number of different kinds of weasels found all over Eurasia, North and Central America, and the Middle East.

30. The badger of Europe and the Near East (*Meles taxus*) is quite unlike our North American animal. Its pelts were of great value to the Hebrews and were extensively used in their sacred tabernacles.

31. Just what monkey (ape) is meant by the writers of the Old Testament is not known, but it is most likely that the Rhesus Monkey of India is implied, as it is said to have arrived with "peacocks and ivory." On the other hand, various baboons were well known in Ancient Egypt.

32. There are half a hundred species of bats indigenous to the Palestinian area. This is a very notable fruit-eating species.

33. Likewise, there are innumerable species of mice found in the area. Apart from the common House Mouse, this wild species is not only common but behaves much like our field mice.

34. The question of the mole-rat in the Bible is a great mystery. There are many kinds of several genera. They are digging animals like moles, and may well have been known to the Hebrews.

35. There are no true rabbits (either *Cuniculus* of Europe or the cottontails—*Sylvilagus*—of the New World) in Palestine. The animals so called by the early English translators of the Bible were hares (*Lepus*), related to our Snowshoes and Jacks.

36. Elephants are mentioned in the Bible only in connection with ivory. There was a large trade in this both from India in the east and via Egypt in the west.

38. Whales are mentioned in the Bible, but in several different contexts. There was a Phoenician whaling industry on the coast of Palestine in ancient times and the whale they pursued was the Sperm Whale shown here.

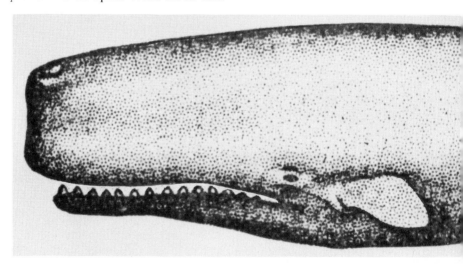

37. The "Feeble Folk," or coneys, of the Bible were the strange little hoofed animals related to elephants, and known to us as hyraxes.

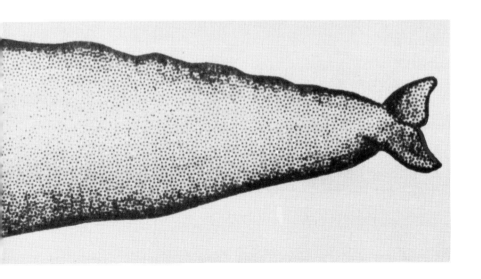

39. There are two species of ostrich. One at least was common in the Biblical lands in early days.

40. Pelicans are thought of—and rightly—as being seacoast divers for small fish. However, they delight in inland lakes, and especially in desert areas, both in the Orient and in our West.

41. The Heron of the Mediterranean is the common species of Europe.

42. Bitterns are mysterious birds in that they are almost perfectly camouflaged but make strange ghostly noises. They appear to have greatly impressed the ancients.

43. Storks are still common features of the Holy Land. Their migratory passages through various countries may have caused their association with human birth.

44. There is much doubt as to whether the swan is actually implied by certain passages in the Bible. Swans were and are indigenous to the area, and they may have been prime game.

45. Kites form a numerous group of small Birds-of-Prey and some are still very numerous in the Bible lands, where they prey on rodents and other small pests.

46. The Golden Eagle has ever been the royal bird of empires. The Ancient Hebrews regarded it in two separate lights—as a symbol of freedom and majesty; and as the national symbol of the hated nations of Mesopotamia.

47. There are at least four quite distinct kinds of vultures found in Palestine and the adjacent countries. This Griffon Vulture was photographed in Israel.

48. Lammergeiers are the largest of the Old World vultures though they are in themselves rather distinct. They are possibly the highest-flying of all birds and awed the ancients.

49. The Osprey is an almost universally distributed fish-eating eagle. It is also one of the most graceful birds in flight.

50. Of hawks and falcons there are many species indigenous to the Mediterranean and Arabian areas. Perhaps the best known is the Peregrine Falcon (or Duck-Hawk), trained since time immemorial to hunt small game for man.

51. There is no doubt that the peacock of India was well known to the early Hebrews. It was regularly imported via Mesopotamia and seems to have been kept as an ornamental pet and for food.

52. There are at least two quite distinct kinds of partridges found in the Palestinian area. One is the Red-legged, the other the Sand. This is the Sand partridge.

53. The tiny Quail (*Coturnix coturnix*) would seem to have suffered the most appalling fate of all animals. For centuries it has migrated annually for great distances but seems always to have been netted by men as food, every time it moved.

54. The origin of the Domestic Fowl—obviously a direct descendant of the wild Jungle Fowl of the Orient—is lost in the mists of prehistory. The Egyptians had them and so did the Israelites.

55. There are many species of cranes distributed throughout the world, and all migrate north-south-to-north annually. The Common Crane of Eurasia (*Grus grus*) passes through Palestine twice a year.

56. The Lapwing is not known to Americans. It is a form of plover common to most of Eurasia. A beautiful bird with a distinctive down-sweeping crest, it is a common marsh bird of Eurasia.

57. What we call the "common pigeon" is really the Rock Dove (*Columba livia*) of the rocky crags of Europe. It has been semi-domesticated since time immemorial, and has been spread all over the world. Today, it comes in dozens of exotic forms. The bird shown here is called a pigeon in Israel today.

57. "The voice of the turtle" in the Bible meant, in actual fact, the cooing of the Turtle Dove (*Streptopelia turtur*) which, like the Rock Dove, was domesticated by man in very ancient times.

58. Many species of cuckoos are distributed almost all over the world. The commonest in western Europe and the Mediterranean is a bird that "parasitizes" other birds, forcing them to rear its young. This shows small foster parent feeding young cuckoo.

59. There are several species of owls in the eastern Mediterranean area and the ancient peoples of that region were much impressed with their strange nocturnal and, to us, curious habits. This is an Eagle Owl (*Bubo bubo*).

60. The Hoopoe (*Upupa epops*) is a beautiful, perky, but somewhat extraordinary bird. The Hebrews did not like its habit of foraging in garbage dumps.

61. The Raven is often said to be the "Top Bird," in that it is the largest and most aggressive of the crow family that, in turn, appears to head the list of all living birds.

62. The Common Swallow of the Mediterranean is a charming little bird (*Hirundo rustica*) that since time immemorial has nested in and on the houses of men. All the ancients felt kindly toward swallows

63. It seems that sparrows, of some kind, are indicated in the Bible in several passages. There are dozens of different kinds found all over the world, but the so-called "English House Sparrow"—actually a weaver-finch—is the best known. They do occur in Palestine today.

64. The question of the "viper" of the Bible is a difficult one to answer. There are several genera of these snakes (*Vipera, Cerastes, Pseudocerastes*, etc.) found in the Bible lands. They are today, and always have been, a considerable menace to travelers in the dry areas, especially travelers without shoes or wearing sandals.

65. There has been much debate as to just what the "asp" was in the early English translations of the Bible. It is now generally agreed that it was, basically, the Egyptian Cobra (*Naja haje*).

66. It seems that some lizard (or lizards) was intended by a few passages in the Bible. There are many forms of mere "lizards" found in the area. This is *Lacerta muralis*, one of the common forms.

66. Skinks are, to the average non-specialist, lizards but they are of a very special type. Mostly they dig in sand, are nocturnal, and move very swiftly.

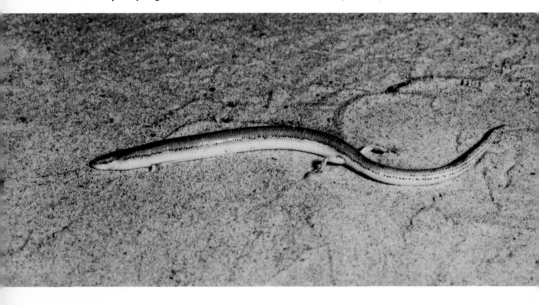

67. One species of true Chameleon is found in the Palestinian area. This is known as *Chameleon communis*. It does change color to a limited extent and this greatly impressed the people of old.

68. There is a gecko common to the Near Eastern region. These animals are lizards but of a very strange type. They can climb up a glass window and walk upside-down on a ceiling.

69. The Nile Crocodile (*Crocodilus niloticus*) was, and still is, a most fearsome beast that accounts for many human lives in Africa. In ancient times, it was very prevalent in the lower Nile and well known to the Hebrews.

70. There are, of course, many kinds of frogs indigenous to the Egypt-to-Armenia area. One of the commonest is what is called in Europe the Common Frog (*Rana esculenta*).

71. "Fish," per se, become of importance in the New Testament. Just which fish were referred to is not known but the Carp has played a prominent part in Hebrew and Christian symbolism.

72. Bees and the honey they provided were an important aspect of the economy of the peoples of the ancient world. In the Bible lands, this appears to have been collected mostly if not entirely from wild bees' nests.

73. The references to the Hornet may seem strange to Americans. The animals referred to by this name, in English, are not the same as those found in the New World. This is a True Hornet, a kind of huge "yellow-jacket."

74. Ants are as widespread and as numerous of kind in the Bible lands as elsewhere. Their industrious habits have always intrigued thinking men.

75. It is highly probable that the "moths" referred to in the Bible were, above all, the Clothes Moth, which indeed does "corrupt" by eating woolen and other clothes.

75. The larva—or caterpillar—of the Clothes Moth is the real destroyer of clothing and other materials. It makes a sort of "sleeping-bag" for itself.

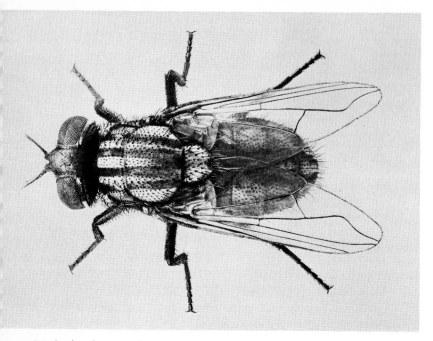

76. Again, there are innumerable species of flies (i.e., Two-winged or True Flies—*Diptera*) in the eastern Mediterrean area, but there, as elsewhere, the Common Housefly (*Musca domestica*) is predominant and a great pest as a disease carrier, and most notably of eye diseases.

77. Several species of mosquitoes are found in Palestine, including the common *Culex* and the yellow-fever carrier *Aedes*. The first British translators of the Bible sometimes used the name "gnats" for these insects, an English term that covers many small kinds of pestilential insects.

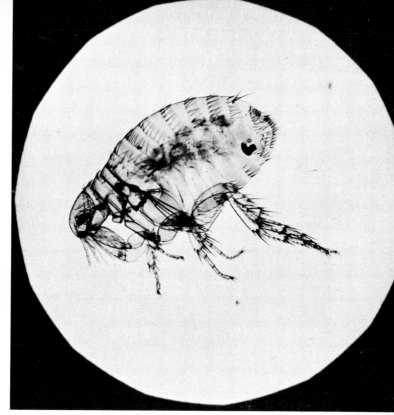

78. Fleas have been a scourge to man since he started living in permanent encampments and houses. In some marvelous way, the Ancient Hebrews seemed to have sensed that they were connected with disease.

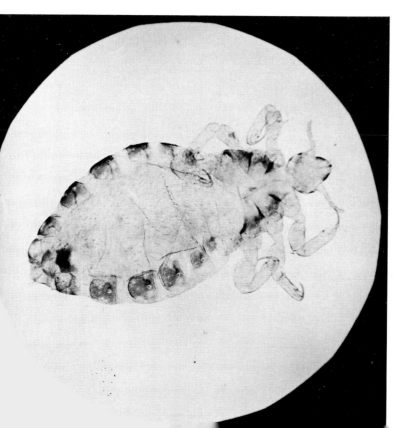

79. The body lice that infested men before our modern age of strict bodily hygiene often multiplied to such proportions that clothing became almost intolerable. The Hebrews were pioneers in the formulation of hygienic counter-measures.

80. Locust plagues swept over the Biblical lands in ancient times as they do today. The country was also sometimes ravished by plagues of mere grasshoppers.

81. The spider seems to have been somewhat respected by the Hebrews as an apparently intelligent destroyer of noxious insects. There are many species found in Palestine.

82. Several species of scorpion are found in Palestine. It has been known from time immemorial that all are potentially hurtful and some highly dangerous.

83. Shells, as opposed to what we call generally "shellfish," are mentioned in the Bible. Ancient Israel, however, was not a coastal nation and shells were looked upon as ornaments.

84. The Horse Leech (*Haemopis sanguisuga*) is mentioned in the Bible and was doubtless well known as an unwelcome inhabitant of wells and water holes.

85. This is the species of coral mentioned in the Bible, according to modern Israeli scholars. It probably came from the Indian Ocean.

86. This is an example of the type of sponge apparently used commercially in ancient times and which would have been used to offer vinegar to Christ on the Cross.

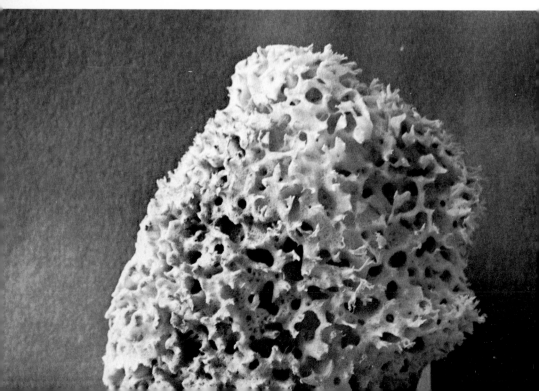

Chapter 7
Mammals of the Bible

[The scientific names of the domestic animals are after E. Laurence Palmer, FIELDBOOK OF NATURAL HISTORY, 1949, and F. E. Zeuner, A HISTORY OF DOMESTICATED ANIMALS, 1963.]

UNGULATES

Equidae	1. Horse	Sus	*Equus caballus*
	2. Mule	Pered	—
	3. Ass (Donkey)	Chámôr	*Equus asinus*
	3. Onager (Wild Ass)	Arodh	*Equus hemionus onager*
Suidae	4. Wild Boar	Chazir b'er	*Sus scrofa scrofa*
	5. Swine	Chazir	*Sus scrofa* (var: **domestica**)
Hippopotam- idae	6. Hippo	Sus ha-yorm	*Hippopotamus amphibius*
Camelidae	7. Camel	Gamal	*Camelus dromedarius*
Cervidae	8. Red Deer	Horah-yoal	*Cervus elephus*
	9. Fallow Deer	Yahmur (?)	*Dama dama*
Bovidae	10. Aurochs	Re'em	*Bos primigenius*
	11. Cattle	Elef, Abbir	*Bos taurus*
Antelopinae	12. Bubal	Yahmur	*Alcelaphus buselaphus*
	13. Addax	Dishon	*Addax nasomaculatus*
	14. Oryx	Têo	*Aegoryx algazel*
	15. Gazelles	Tsvi	*Gazella arabica, G. dorcas*
Ovidae	16. Sheep	Tzon	*Ovis aries*
	17. Aoudad	Zemer	*Ammotragus lervia*
Caprinae	18. Ibex	Ako	*Capra nubiana*
	19. Goat	Ya'el	*Capra hircus*

CARNI- VORES

Felidae	20. Lion	Ari	*Panthera leo*
	21. Leopard	Namer	*Panthera pardus*
	22. Cat (Domestic)	Chatul	*Felis domesticus*
Ursidae	23. Bear	Dob	*Ursus syriacus*
Canidae	24. Wolf	Zeeb	*Canis lupus*
	25. Dog	Keleb	*Canis familiaris*
	26. Jackal	Than, Iyyim	*Thos aureus*
	27. Fox	Shu'al	*Vulpes aegyptiaca*
Hyaenidae	28. Hyena	Zabua	*Hyaena hyaena*
Mustelidae	29. Weasel	Choled	*Mustela* sp., *Poecilictis* sp.
	30. Badger	Takhash	*Meles taxus*

PRIMATES

	31. Ape	Køf	(unknown)

BATS

	32. Bat	Atellef	(numerous)

RODENTS

	33. Mouse	Akbar	*Mus musculus* and others
	34. Mole-Rat	Chephor-peroth	*Spalax* sp.

LAGO-
  MORPHS

	35. Hare	Arnebeth	*Lepus syriacus*

PROBOSCID-
  EANS

	36. Elephant	Pil	*Elephas indicus, Loxodonta* spp.

HYRAXES

	37. Hyrax	Shāphān	*Procavia syriaca*

CETACEANS

	38. Whales	Tanninim	(Larger whales)

We will now discuss the animals listed above one at a time, and in the particular sequence in which they are arranged in that list. This is, in scientific parlance, their systematic order, the method adopted for the classification of all animals and plants; it is the only one which brings like animals together, and thus as far as possible represents relationships. The order is roughly a descent from the most highly evolved in the sense of complexity to ever more simple forms. (The mammals come first.)

It was once customary to start the mammals with the Great Apes, but the modern findings of comparative anatomists have shown that the so-called Primates (lemurs, monkeys, and apes) are really very primitive, generalized forms. They are in many respects not far removed from the basic mammalian plan. On the other hand, animals that have hoofs (known as the *Ungulata*) are very specialized. Thus most modern systematic accounts of the mammals either begin with the Ungulates and end with the Platypus, or the reverse, for such over-all descriptions may run either one way or the other without loss of clarity. We begin with the hoofed mammals.

HOOFED MAMMALS (Superorder, *Ungulata*)

The Ungulates are entirely adapted to life on land, with toes which are in most cases enclosed in solid, horny hoofs. A few forms, however, are provided with broad, flat nails. In all living members of the order the number of functional toes is reduced from five to four, three, two, or even one. Although a few generalized forms are omnivorous, all of the more specialized Ungulates feed strictly on vegetation. To facilitate crushing of leaves and branches, the cheek teeth are equipped with broad crowns and often with a complex system of ridges. Many members of the order are characterized by the development of horns. As will be seen, these horns vary greatly in both size and shape, and very often are found only on the male members of the species. Ungulates are divided into two very unequal major groups according to whether they have an odd or an even number of toes. The former are called the *Perissodactyla* and the latter the *Artiodactyla.* (These long words mean odd and even number of toes, in a Latinized form of Greek.) The first group today contains only the Rhinoceroses, the Tapirs, and the Horse Tribe.

This tribe contains the true horses, both wild and domestic, the donkeys or asses, and the zebras. The horse and the ass have probably played a more important role in the history of man than any other animals.

THE HORSE FAMILY (*Equidae*)

The chief characteristic that sets this group apart from other mammals is that in all existing forms the number of toes on each foot is reduced to one. This single toe, which in the fore-leg corresponds to the human middle finger and in the hind-leg to the middle toe, is supported on the end of a long cannon bone. In most forms, small splints on either side of the cannon bone are the remnants of the digits on either side which have been lost in the process of evolution. The animals are well adapted for grazing, and in the wild state they travel in large groups over open plains and grasslands.

1. Horses

"And they brought their cattle unto Joseph: and Joseph gave them bread *in exchange* for horses, and for the flocks, and for the cattle of the herds, and for the asses: and he fed them with bread for all their cattle for that year" (Gen. 47:17).

"And they brought every man his present, vessels of silver, and vessels of gold, and garments, and armour, and spices, horses, and mules, a rate year by year" (I Kings 10:25).

"And David took from him a thousand chariots, and seven thousand horsemen, and twenty thousand footmen: David also houghed all the chariot *horses,* but reserved of them an hundred chariots" (I Chron. 18:4).

"Hast thou given the horse strength? hast thou clothed his neck with thunder? Canst thou make him afraid as a grasshopper? the glory of his nostrils *is* terrible. He paweth in the valley, and rejoiceth in *his* strength: he goeth on to meet the armed men. He mocketh at fear, and is not affrighted; neither turneth he back from the sword. The quiver rattleth against him, the glittering spear and the shield. He swalloweth the ground with fierceness and rage; neither believeth he that *it is* the sound of the trumpet. He saith among the trumpets, Ha, ha; and he smelleth the battle afar off, the thunder of the captains, and the shouting" (Job 39:19–25).

"An horse *is* a vain thing for safety: neither shall he deliver *any* by his great strength" (Ps. 33:17).

"I have compared thee, O my love, to a company of horses in Pharaoh's chariots" (Song of Sol. 1:9).

Horses are named 153 times in the Bible, horsemen are named 61 times, horseback 5 times, horsehoofs once. Several Hebrew words are used by the different Biblical writers to signify the horse representing the different qualities of the animals just as our words do today; e.g.: "charger," "pony," "mare," etc.

The chief distinction of the horse in Biblical days lay in its value for purposes of war. Not only was it splendid for riding but it was also necessary for pulling the heavy, springless war chariots. Naturally, these two functions required different kinds of animals. This difference is clearly revealed in Scripture, for the Hebrews used the word *Sus* for chariot horses and *Parash* for cavalry horses.

It is interesting to note that almost all of the Scriptural references to the horse refer to its functions in war. There is a surprising lack of detail about the animal, particularly concerning its personal qualities. It is remarkable that even the Book of Proverbs, which is so rich in the description of various animals, makes very little mention of the horse.

Early in the Israelites' history, they were prohibited by Mosaic law from the breeding of horses, but the demands of war caused both David and Solomon to import horses from Egypt and to breed them, thus disregarding the command against a plurality of horses just as they did the one against a plurality of wives.

Horses as a group were evolved in North America, but the original habitat of the wild horses that gave rise to the domesticated breeds remains controversial. The majority of naturalists hold that the horses of Mesopotamia, Palestine, and Egypt originated somewhere in Central Asia. It is thought that the horse then spread eastward to Mongolia and the northern plains of China; southwestward into Persia, India, and Arabia, whence it was taken by man into Egypt and North Africa. The same type of horse also appeared at an early date in Greece and then fanned out along the northern shores of the Mediterranean. Western Europe had its own species. It was not until about the third millennium B.C. that the horse was first domesticated, probably in southwestern Siberia. The first historical record is on a Babylonian tablet of the period of Hammurabi, about 2100 B.C., and the horse is referred to as "the ass from the East." Horses are also depicted in some of the cave paintings discovered in southern France dated thousands of years before this, but these were unquestionably wild horses, like the other beasts shown in the cave paintings. Domestication took place independently in three areas: southwestern Asia (the Tarpan); Mongolia (Przewalski's Horse); and western Europe (the European Wild Horse). Ancient Chinese records suggest that the horse was first tamed there as an addition to the food supply.

The shepherd kings of the Hyksos Dynasties probably brought the horse to Egypt. The Egyptians thus already had the horse when the Children of Israel moved to Egypt.

When the Romans conquered Britain, they found a native breed of horse already on the island, with which their heavier horses interbred. Some authorities contend that the Exmoor pony is a descendant of the original British stock, although it is generally considered that other blood, either by accident or by design, was introduced from time to time. William the Conqueror's horse was of Spanish blood, while chargers of various types were ridden by his men. When the Crusaders returned from the Holy Land they brought further new blood, including the Arab, and history relates that Charles II sent emissaries abroad to get new stock for the royal stud.

As a result of these centuries of selective breeding from a wide range of mixed stock—the best available from many different countries—Britain ultimately produced the great variety and high quality seen today, from the Shire horse, standing over 17 hands and weighing a ton, to the Shetland pony of 8 or 9 hands. (The "hand" used by horsemen to determine size measures 4 inches.)

Despite the inroads of mechanization, the horse is used even today for a great number of purposes—for work, for pleasure, and for ceremonial occasions.

The breed distinctions in horses, apart from the four main breeds of heavy draught horses—the Shire, Clydesdale, Suffolk Punch, and Percheron—are not as definite as those typical of the cows. Even the Thoroughbred, which is a definite variety bred for speed, is found in considerable variation in both color and size. The same applies to Hackney horses and Hunters.

The word "pony" is so vague as to be almost meaningless, since it is commonly applied to a whole series of small horses ranging from a tiny Shetland to a polo pony standing nearly 5 feet high. Some authorities in the field insist that no less than 8 distinct types are recognized by serious horse breeders—namely, Highland, Dales, Shetland, Fell, Dartmoor, Exmoor, New Forest, and Welsh. The Welsh pony is probably the strongest animal in the world in proportion to its size, reputedly able to pull 27 times its own weight. (An elephant is estimated to be able to haul 4 times its own weight.)

2. Mule

"And these *are* the children of Zibeon; both Ajah, and Anah: this *was that* Anah that found the mules in the wilderness, as he fed the asses of Zibeon his father" (Gen. 36:24).

"And the servants of Absalom did unto Amnon as Absalom had commanded. Then all the king's sons arose, and every man gat him up upon his mule, and fled" (II Sam. 13:29).

"And they brought every man his present, vessels of silver, and vessels of gold, and garments, and armour, and spices, horses, and mules, a rate year by year" (I Kings 10:25).

"Be ye not as the horse, *or* as the mule, *which* have no understanding; whose mouth must be held in with bit and bridle, lest they come near unto thee" (Ps. 32:9).

"They of the house of Togarmah traded in thy fairs with horses, and horsemen, and mules" (Ezek. 27:14).

"And so shall be the plague of the horse, of the mule, of the camel, and of the ass, and of all the beasts that shall be in these tents, as this plague" (Zech. 14:15).

The mule is named 22 times in the Bible, although it is mentioned only once before the time of King David.

The mule is the result of crossing a jackass and a mare. This hybrid makes a most useful animal, combining the size and strength of the horse with the patience, endurance, and sure-footedness of the donkey. The production of mules goes back to prehistoric times; the crossbreeding is believed to have been tried very soon after the domestication of the horse. The Greeks and Romans used mules extensively for centuries. The animals seem to thrive best in hot, dry climates.

The mule was held in high esteem by the Israelites. It was not long after it became known in the Holy Land that it superseded the ass as a riding animal for princes and kings and other people of rank.

Despite its use as a riding animal for royalty, the mule was still employed for the mundane task of transporting burdens. These divergent roles, however, can be explained by the different types of mules employed for each task. A special and costly type of handsome mules, probably much like those of Andalusia, was reserved for the saddle, while the smaller and less beautiful mules were employed as beasts of burden. Even today mules are quite common in the Bible lands as work animals, particularly for simple farming.

Mules have no offspring. They have been described rather cynically as "without pride of ancestry or hope of posterity," inasmuch as they are sterile in both sexes. Some ancient writers have made references to fertile mules, and similar claims have been made by others from time to time, but they are not generally accepted. Mules must be bred from the male ass and a mare; when the sexes of the parents are in the opposite order, the offspring is of little value because of its inferior size, and is called a "hinny."

Mules have long enjoyed a reputation for obstinacy, but the Bible, surprisingly, makes no mention of the trait.

3. Ass

"And if a man shall open a pit, or if a man shall dig a pit, and not cover it, and an ox or an ass fall therein; The owner of the pit shall make *it* good, *and* give money unto the owner of them; and the dead *beast* shall be his" (Exod. 21:33–34).

"Speak, ye that ride on white asses, ye that sit in judgment, and walk by the way" (Judg. 5:10).

"And he had forty sons and thirty nephews, that rode on threescore and ten ass colts: and he judged Israel eight years" (Judg. 12:14).

"For vain man would be wise, though man be born *like* a wild ass's colt" (Job 11:12).

"A whip for the horse, a bridle for the ass, and a rod for the fool's back" (Prov. 26:3).

"The oxen likewise, and the young asses that ear the ground, shall eat clean provender, which hath been winnowed with the shovel and with the fan" (Isa. 30:24).

The ass was a very valuable animal in Biblical cultures. The Bible describes both the domesticated and the wild ass, the former being useful as a work animal and the latter, known as the Onager, as a hunter's prize.

The origin of asses found in Palestine is uncertain. Probably they derived from the African rather than any Asiatic wild form. It is interesting to note that Webster's Dictionary suggests that the word "ass" may be of Semitic origin from the Hebrew word *athon.*

Asses were domesticated even earlier than horses or camels. Monuments have been found from the early Sumerian civilization, about 4200 B.C., which depict the ass. On the whole, the Eastern ass is a more graceful and handsome creature than the one found in America and Western Europe.

The possession of asses was a mark of a man's wealth in Biblical days. In determining the riches of an Israelite, asses had the same rank as other domestic animals such as sheep, cattle, camels, and goats. Their value consisted in their uses as burden bearers, for riding, and as a source of food. Asses were employed to carry the household goods when the nomadic peoples of the Near East changed location. Asses also carried a heavy work load by drawing plows, raising water from the wells, and turning millstones to grind the grain.

The ass was used as a riding animal and men of wealth would ride the superior asses. White asses were considered to be the swiftest and strongest, and therefore were greatly prized. Men of rank such as judges rode on white asses (Judg. 5:10).

She-asses were valuable for their production of the young and for milk. Asses' milk has always been a common food in the Holy Land, and is thought to be particularly beneficial for people with tubercular, scrofulous, and dyspeptic disorders.

That the ass was a highly prized beast in Biblical Palestine is evident from the fact that it is mentioned over 130 times in the Scriptures, and also from the fact that Hebrew, a language not noted for its extensive vocabulary, has a number of words to designate the beast, depending on color, age, sex, etc. The most common of these names is *hámôr*, meaning "reddish," the most common color of the Eastern ass.

An early custom which still prevails is to paint the most shapely and valuable donkeys in stripes of various colors.

In many parts of the Near East the pedigrees of the best breeds of asses are carefully preserved.

The customary mode of riding the ass was to place a cloth on the animal's back, on which the owner then sat. If an entire family was traveling, the women and children rode while the father walked alongside. This has been popularized by Christian painters in depicting the flight of the Holy Family into Egypt.

According to Flavius Josephus, the Jewish historian, the ass was used in the Near East in the threshing of wheat.

From both the Scriptures (Isa. 21:7) and Greek writers we learn that part of the Persian and probably also the Syrian cavalry used asses for war. Nothing of this sort existed among the Hebrews, where the animal was retained only for peaceful uses; in fact, it was a symbol of peace just as the horse was a symbol of war.

The ass was considered "unclean" by the early Jews and the eating of its flesh was forbidden by law. However, in times of famine, necessity sometimes took precedence over the law, for we find in II Kings 6:25 that during the reign of Joram, when Benadad laid siege to Samaria, the head of an ass was sold for 80 pieces of silver—more than twice what Judas received for Christ.

The names for the wild ass are found in the Old Testament. These are *péré* and *arodh*. It is not known if they refer to two species, or if one is the original Hebrew and the other Aramaic. The wild ass or Onager, which is larger and more shapely than the domestic, is one of the most untamable of animals. It survives today only in northern Iran and Afghanistan.

THE PIG FAMILY (*Suidae*)

The pigs or swine make up a very familiar group that differs in many respects from the other Ungulates. Probably their most conspicuous characteristic is a truncated mobile snout, terminating in a disk-shaped surface on which the nostrils are located. The terminal disk is supported by an additional small, separate bone (called the prenasal) at the end of the skull. Although each foot is composed of four completely developed toes, the middle pair are the largest and most functionally important. Their inner surfaces are flattened and have the appearance of a cloven hoof. Most swine have large tusks in both jaws which grow continuously throughout life. The tusks of the upper jaw are unique in that they curve upward instead of pointing downward, as in other animals.

4. The Wild Boar

"The boar out of the wood doth waste it, and the wild beast of the field doth devour it" (Ps. 80:13).

The wild boar is specifically referred to only in this one passage from the Psalms. It is used figuratively to represent a destructive foe. The word "beast" in this passage probably also refers to the boar to complete the parallel structure of the verse.

The boar is probably the best possible example of a destructive animal. A party of wild hogs can destroy an entire vineyard or a field of crops in a single night. They devour, trample, and ravage everything within reach.

Wild boars were once common throughout Palestine, and they were particularly abundant in the mountainous regions of Lebanon and Anti-Lebanon, the cavernous Jordan Valley, and in wooded sections such as Mount Tabor. The boar population has been greatly reduced in Palestine since the forests have been cut away and the land more widely cultivated.

The law of the Old Testament forbade the Jews to eat swine flesh, but in the early days the people had eaten it. The flesh of the wild boar is a superior meat to that of tame swine. In later times, as indicated in the New Testament, some Jews probably violated this law by eating swine, and it appears that some even raised them.

5. Swine

"And the swine, because it divideth the hoof, yet cheweth not the cud, it *is* unclean unto you: ye shall not eat of their flesh, nor touch their dead carcase" (Deut. 14:8).

"*As* a jewel of gold in a swine's snout, *so is* a fair woman which is without discretion" (Prov. 11:22).

"Which remain among the graves, and lodge in the monuments; which eat swine's flesh, and broth of abominable *things is in* their vessels" (Isa. 65:4).

"He that killeth an ox *is as if* he slew a man; he that sacrificeth a lamb, *as if* he cut off a dog's neck; he that offereth an oblation, *as if he offered* swine's blood; he that burneth incense, *as if* he blessed an idol. Yea, they have chosen their own ways, and their soul delighteth in their abomination" (Isa. 66:3).

"Give not that which is holy unto the dogs, neither cast ye your pearls before swine, lest they trample them under their feet, and turn again and rend you" (Matt. 7:6).

"But it is happened unto them according to the true proverb, The dog *is* turned to his own vomit again; and the sow that was washed, to her wallowing in the mire" (II Pet. 2:22).

The word "swine" is used 20 times in Scripture, although the words "hog" and "pig" are never used. It is difficult to understand the intensity of the ancient Hebrews' hatred of swine. The older, stricter Jews would not even mention the name of the animal, but would always substitute in its place the term "the abomination."

The Israelites considered themselves polluted if they were even touched by a swine's bristle. Since the Jews hated the swine so fiercely, it seems strange that the latter was found in such abundance in Palestine. One would have thought they would have been exterminated, but instead they roamed the plains and the hills of the Holy Land in huge herds. At times they were even herded by the less strict Jews.

It has been a general belief in countries with hot climates that the flesh of swine is unclean and may be a direct cause of various diseases. Leprosy was one disease which many attributed to the eating of pork.

During the days of the Apocrypha, when Antiochus Epiphanes, the Syrian, had captured the Holy Land, the Israelites were forced to offer swine upon their altars for religious sacrifice and then to eat the flesh. The Greeks, to whom pork was a great delicacy, also forced the Jews to eat swine's flesh in an effort to Hellenize them. Many of the Jews suffered martyrdom for refusing to break their laws by eating pork. The story is told of one mother who saw her seven sons killed for refusing to eat hog's meat, and then was herself martyred for adhering to the ancient laws of her people regarding swine's flesh.

THE HIPPO FAMILY (*Hippopotamidae*)

Of all the Ungulates, the hippopotamus or "river horse" is the best adapted for a partially aquatic life. With their lungs filled with air, their large bulky bodies have a specific gravity exactly equal to that of water, thus enabling the beasts to float at the surface almost indefinitely. Their nostrils are located on the upper surface of a large, transversely expanded muzzle which bears no trace of the terminal disk found in the *Suidae*. Both the nostrils and ears can be closed at will when the animals are submerged. The feet are equipped with four short, well-developed toes which are partially connected by webs. The hippopotami have rough, enormously thick skin that is devoid of hair, except for a few bristles on the head, neck, and tail.

6. Hippopotamus

"Behold now behemoth, which I made with thee; he eateth grass as an ox. Lo now, his strength *is* in his loins, and his force *is* in the navel of his belly. He moveth his tail like a cedar: the sinews of his stones are wrapped together. His bones *are as* strong pieces of brass; his bones *are* like bars of iron. He *is* the chief of the ways of God: he that made him can make his sword to approach *unto him*. Surely the mountains bring him forth food, where all the beasts of the field play. He lieth under the shady trees, in the covert of the reed, and fens. The shady trees cover him *with* their shadow; the willows of the brook compass him about. Behold, he drinketh up a river, *and* hasteth not: he trusteth that he can draw up Jordan into his mouth. He taketh it with his eyes: *his* nose pierceth through snares" (Job 40:15–24).

Bible scholars were once divided as to whether this lengthy passage in Job, the only Scriptural reference to the behemoth, referred to the elephant or the hippopotamus. Both of these animals are thick-skinned creatures known as pachyderms. Today commentators and naturalists agree that the hippopotamus is the animal intended by the word "behemoth."

The passage in Job does not describe an elephant, for the latter does not lie among the reeds and fens, nor does it eat grass like an ox. Also, it seems unlikely that any description of an elephant would fail to refer to the uniqueness of its trunk.

The passage seems to describe a hippopotamus perfectly. The description of the anatomy, place of habitation, and drinking habits all point to a hippopotamus. Furthermore, the Egyptian word for behemoth means "river ox," and the English word "hippopotamus" means river horse.

The hippopotamus is an extremely difficult animal to kill. As indicated in the Scriptural passage, snares are often set in the path of the animal with a spear poised above. When the hippopotamus strikes the rope the spear falls and severs its spinal cord. Another method of killing a hippopotamus is to dig a pitfall at the place where the animal leaves the water at night. The pitfall is camouflaged, and sharp stakes are placed at the bottom.

Excavations in Egypt have revealed that spears were also used to kill the hippopotamus. Repeated harpooning would eventually weaken a hippopotamus and cause it to bleed to death. Arrows cannot penetrate the thick hide of this mammoth animal, and so are effective only if shot through the eye into the brain.

Though a bulky animal of great weight, the hippopotamus could not be used for food by the Israelites because it was neither cloven-hoofed nor a cud-chewer. Furthermore, it was not found in Palestine.

THE CAMEL FAMILY (*Camelidae*)

The *Camelidae* are represented in the New World by the llamas, and in the Old World by the one- and two-humped camels. Because the camels are well suited to life in dry, desolate areas, they have proved valuable to man as beasts of burden in the deserts of Africa, Arabia, and central Asia. The group is characterized by a relatively large body with long, powerful legs which terminate in two-toed feet. The vertebrae which comprise the neck are greatly elongated in relation to the rest of the body, and the upper lip is split much like that of a hare. The stomach is divided into three sections, the first two of which are equipped with a number of pouches which can be closed by the action of muscles, and which are used to store water. Camels are also able to store up food, which takes the form of large fatty humps on their backs.

7. *Camel (Dromedary)*

"And he entreated Abram well for her sake; and he had sheep, and oxen, and he asses, and menservants, and maidservants, and she asses, and camels" (Gen. 12:16).

"And they sat down to eat bread: and they lifted up their eyes and looked, and, behold, a company of Ishmeelites came from Gilead, with their camels bearing spicery and balm and myrrh, going to carry *it* down to Egypt" (Gen. 37:25).

"Then Zebah and Zalmunna said, Rise thou, and fall upon us; for as the man *is, so is* his strength. And Gideon arose, and slew Zebah and Zalmunna, and took away the ornaments that *were* on their camels' necks" (Judg. 8:21).

"And he wrote in the king Ahasuerus' name, and sealed *it* with the king's ring; and sent letters by posts on horseback, *and* riders on mules, camels, *and* young dromedaries . . ." (Esther 8:10).

"His substance also was seven thousand sheep, and three thousand camels, and five hundred yoke of oxen, and five hundred she asses, and a very great household; so that this man was the greatest of all the men of the east" (Job 1:3).

"And their camels shall be a booty, and the multitude of their cattle a spoil; and I will scatter into all winds them *that are* in the utmost corners; and I will bring their calamity from all sides thereof, saith the Lord" (Jer. 49:32).

The camel, one of the first animals to be mentioned in the Bible, was ranked in importance with sheep, cattle, and asses in Old Testament days. Of the 66 references to the camel, one third list the animal with all or two of these other animals.

Camels were valuable in the Holy Land because of their amazing adaptability to desert life. They are a hardy breed that can stand great privations of food and water. Further value lay in their varied usage. They were used for riding, transporting goods, for agricultural work, and for their products, such as milk, wool, hair, dung, and leather.

Camel trains were the common means of commercial transport between Arabia, Egypt, and Assyria. In fact, the camel is still commonly used in the Near East for desert travel. In Biblical days, Petra, now famous for the grandeur of its ruins, was the center of the caravan routes that crossed the desert to the ports on the Mediterranean, the Persian Gulf, and the Red Sea. Petra lies near Mount Hor, where the priest Aaron died. It was accessible in those days only by camel because of its rugged terrain and narrow passes.

Every land-owning farmer had at least one camel to help him. They were an invaluable source of aid, for they could carry heavy loads of harvested grain, draw the plow, turn the waterwheel for irrigation purposes, and drag the threshing board.

The products of the camel's body had varied uses. The camel's hair was woven into a thick cloth which was used to make heavy mantles for bad weather, cordage, sackcloth, carpets, and tent curtains. The hair of one camel might weigh as much as 10 pounds. The best quality of hair for weaving purposes is found about the hump. The camel's dung, in addition to being used for fuel, is an ingredient in roofing. The milk of the camel is a rich, strong drink that usually is curdled. Butter and cheese are also made from camel's milk.

According to Hebrew law the camel was an unclean animal, and therefore could not be eaten. But many of the neighboring nomadic tribes would eat camels, particularly when stranded on a desert. Water, in addition to food, would be yielded from the dead camel's stomach reservoirs in an emergency.

The name Dromedary, often applied to the Arabian or One-humped Camel as if it were a synonym, denotes only a very special type or breed; a long-legged, lightly built riding camel as opposed to the heavier pack animal. It is interesting to note that this fact was recognized in ancient times and that a distinction is made in the book of Esther, as quoted above.

THE DEER FAMILY (*Cervidae*)

Including such forms as the deer, elk, moose, and reindeer, the *Cervidae* constitute one of the most distinctive groups of mammals. The chief and most obvious characteristic of most species is the annual development in the males of large, branched antlers. Only in the reindeer are they found in both sexes. When fully developed, the antlers are devoid of any covering of skin or horn, and for all practical purposes may be regarded as a mass of dead bone carried for a certain time by a living animal. The end of the muzzle is naked in all species. The *Cervidae* belong to a division of Ungulates known as Ruminants, for they possess certain peculiarities in stomach construction and digestion. The stomach is divided into a series of compartments, some of which are used to store partially chewed food. The food is later regurgitated, rechewed, and finally swallowed into a section of the stomach where true digestion takes place.

8. Red Deer (*Hart and Hind*)

"Notwithstanding thou mayest kill and eat flesh in all thy gates, whatsoever thy soul lusteth after, according to the blessing of the Lord thy God which he hath given thee: the unclean and the clean may eat thereof, as of the roebuck, and as of the hart" (Deut. 12:15).

"Ten fat oxen, and twenty oxen out of the pastures, and a hundred sheep, beside harts, and roebucks, and fallowdeer, and fatted fowl" (I Kings 4:23).

"As the hart panteth after the water brooks, so panteth my soul after thee, O God" (Ps. 42:1).

"My beloved *is* like a roe or a young hart: behold, he standeth behind our wall, he looketh forth at the windows, shewing himself through the lattice" (Song of Sol. 2:9).

"Then shall the lame *man* leap as an hart, and the tongue of the dumb sing: for in the wilderness shall waters break out, and streams in the desert" (Isa. 35:6).

"And from the daughter of Zion all her beauty is departed: her princes are become like harts *that* find no pasture; and they are gone without strength before the pursuer" (Lam. 1:6).

The hart, or male Red Deer (*Cervus elephas*), is referred to 11 times in the Bible, and it seems evident from these allusions that it was an animal both plentiful and valuable in Biblical days.

Only the hart and not the hind, the female red deer, was listed for food. Although its flesh was probably not as good as that of the Fallow Deer, the Bible reports that it was daily fare at Solomon's royal table.

The Psalmist, in speaking of the hart's panting, employs a word used only one other time in the entire Bible. He was referring to the strange braying of the hart when it was in an agony of thirst during a drought.

The hart is used in the Song of Solomon to portray the lover of the bride. The animal is probably utilized for such symbolism because of its grace, beauty, and fleetness.

The hind is mentioned 10 times in the Bible. Three of the passages speak of the hind's feet, probably referring to the animal's graceful movements. The writers may also have had in mind the hind's sure-footedness, for she can safely traverse the most rugged mountain terrain. The hind was obviously well respected by the Israelites. Although the hart was allowed as food, the hind was not.

Several names are derived from the Hebrew word for hind, *ayyalah*. Ayalon was the name of one or more cities in Palestine, and it meant "the place of deer." Today a place with a similar name exists only 14 miles from Jerusalem. It is called Yalo and means "doe or wild she-goat." *Ophrah*, meaning hind or fawn, was the name of both a man and two towns (Josh. 18:23, Judg. 6:11). The title of Psalm 22 uses the expression *Aijeleth Shahar*, which meant "hind of the dawn," probably a popular tune which David's psalm was to follow. This phrase refers to the hind's habit of searching for food at the break of day.

9. *Fallow Deer*

"And Isaac loved Esau, because he did eat of *his* venison; but Rebekah loved Jacob" (Gen. 25:28).

"Now therefore take, I pray thee, thy weapons, thy quiver and thy bow, and go out to the field, and take me *some* venison . . ." (Gen. 27:3).

"These *are* the beasts which ye shall eat: the ox, the sheep, and the goat, The hart, and the roebuck, and the fallow deer, and the wild goat, and the pygarg, and the wild ox, and the chamois" (Deut. 14:4–5).

"And Solomon's provision for one day was thirty measures of fine flour, and threescore measures of meal, Ten fat oxen, and twenty oxen out of the pastures, and an hundred sheep, beside harts, and roebucks, and fallowdeer, and fatted fowl" (I Kings 4:22–23).

The fallow deer is listed in the Bible as one of the chief wild animals that was clean, and therefore available to the Israelites as food. The Hebrew word in the Bible for this animal was *yahmur*. It is not certain that "fallow deer" is really the proper translation, for some scholars feel that other animals were intended. Since the fallow deer was not able to live in the southern regions of Palestine around Sinai because of its need for ample amounts of food and water, it is hardly possible that this was the animal named by Moses. Fallow deer were found only in northern Palestine.

Some scholars have suggested that *yahmur* should be translated as "roebuck," but there is doubt as to whether this animal ever inhabited the area. Many Biblical scholars believe that the Bubal, actually a harte-beeste, an antelope also known as the "wild cow" to the Arabs, was the animal intended by the word *yahmur*. The Bubal lived in the arid areas of Egypt, on the border of the Sahara desert, and may then have extended into northern Arabia, the Sinai region and southern Palestine. Therefore, it could have easily been the animal that supplied venison to the Israelites during their wilderness wanderings.

Regardless of what animal was intended, the *yahmur* formed a large portion of the Israelites' meat diet. It was even part of the daily supply for King Solomon's table, and apparently was one of the dainties at any great banquet held by the Israelites.

The Ox Family (*Bovidae*)

Comprising the largest and most important group of ungulates, the family *Bovidae* gathers together such animals as cattle, bison, sheep, ante-lope, gazelles, and goats. As in the *Cervidae*, the most outstanding charac-teristic of this group is the existence, in the male (and sometimes also in the female), of some sort of horns which, however, differ from those of the deer tribe in both structure and form. The horns are formed by a pair of bony projections from the skull that in life are covered with hollow sheaths of horn which are never branched and not shed. They vary in size and shape from the simple spikes of the duikers to the enormous structures of buffalos and large antelope. In some domestic forms of cattle, sheep, and goats horns may be lacking in both sexes. One tiny antelope and one domestic breed of sheep have four. The *Bovidae* also make up the largest group of ruminating animals. The stomach is divided into four chambers, and the process of regurgitating the food for additional chewing is known as "chewing the cud."

Subfamily *Bovinae*

These are large, heavy-bodied ruminants with horns in both sexes. The muzzle is broad, naked, and moist; the tail is usually long and tufted. Included are the aurochs, and all other forms of cattle, including the yak, gaur, banteng, and couprey, the buffalos, and the bison.

10. The Aurochs (or Urus)

"God brought him forth out of Egypt; he hath as it were the strength of an unicorn: he shall eat up the nations his enemies, and shall break their bones, and pierce *them* through with his arrows" (Num. 24:8).

"His glory *is like* the firstling of his bullock, and his horns *are like* the horns of unicorns: with them he shall push the people together to the ends of the earth: and they *are* the ten thousands of Ephraim, and they *are* the thousands of Manasseh" (Deut. 33:17).

"Will the unicorn be willing to serve thee, or abide by thy crib? Canst thou bind the unicorn with his band in the furrow? or will he harrow the valleys after thee? Wilt thou trust him, because his strength *is* great? or wilt thou leave thy labour to him? Wilt thou believe him, that he will bring home thy seed, and gather *it into* thy barn?" (Job 39:9–12).

"Save me from the lion's mouth: for thou hast heard me from the horns of the unicorns" (Ps. 22:21).

"But my horn shalt thou exalt like *the horn of* an unicorn: I shall be anointed with fresh oil" (Ps. 92:10).

"And the unicorns shall come down with them, and the bullocks with the bulls; and their land shall be soaked with blood, and their dust made fat with fatness" (Isa. 34:7).

The word "unicorn" is used 9 times in 8 different Scriptural passages, but, as the poet Wordsworth said, "the word unicorn ought to be expunged from our version of the Bible in all places where it occurs." It is an obviously wrong translation of the Hebrew word *re'em.* The one-horned monster of classical mythology had no relation to the animal intended by the Biblical writers under this name. Apparently, the animal concerned was one perfectly well known to the Israelites, for abundant detail of its qualities and habits are given in these passages.

The Jewish Bible translates the word *re'em* as "buffalo," and there is no doubt that this was generally the type of animal intended. Today, nearly all Bible scholars and naturalists are agreed that the animal meant was the Aurochs, Urus, or Wild Ox (*Bos primigenius*) which is now extinct.

The Urus can be distinguished from a modern ox by its curious horns (see picture). Apparently these were often used as drinking vessels by the Israelites, and some were large enough to hold 4 gallons.

The enormous size of the animal caused Julius Caesar to remark in his famous *Commentaries* that "the Uri are little inferior to elephants in size, but are bulls in their nature, color, and figure."

This comparison with the elephant by Caesar was apparently justified, for a curious Rabbinical legend exists which portrays the Urus as being too large to pass through the door of Noah's Ark. Therefore, it was necessary for Noah to tie a rope to the Urus' huge horns and to tow the animal behind the ark.

11. Cattle

"And Abram *was* very rich in cattle, in silver, and in gold. And he went on his journeys from the south even to Beth-el, unto the place where his tent had been at the beginning, between Beth-el and Hai; Unto the place of the altar, which he had made there at the first: and there Abram called on the name of the Lord. And Lot also, which went with Abram, had flocks, and herds, and tents. And the land was not able to bear them, that they might dwell together: for their substance was great, so that they could not dwell together. And there was a strife between the herdmen of Abram's cattle, and the herdmen of Lot's cattle: and the Canaanite and the Perizzite dwelled then in the land" (Gen. 13:2-7).

"For the children of Joseph were two tribes, Manasseh and Ephraim: therefore they gave no part unto the Levites in the land, save cities to dwell *in*, with their suburbs for their cattle and for their substance" (Josh. 14:4).

"So David and his men went to Keilah, and fought with the Philistines, and brought away their cattle, and smote them with a great slaughter. So David saved the inhabitants of Keilah" (I Sam. 23:5).

"Also the firstborn of our sons, and of our cattle, as *it is* written in the law, and the firstlings of our herds and of our flocks, to bring to the house of our God, unto the priests that minister in the house of our God . . ." (Neh. 10:36).

"I got *me* servants and maidens, and had servants born in my house; also I had great possessions of great and small cattle above all that were in Jerusalem before me . . ." (Eccles. 2:7).

"How do the beasts groan! the herds of cattle are perplexed, because they have no pasture; yea, the flocks of sheep are made desolate" (Joel 1:18).

Many names are used in the Bible to describe the members of the bovine family. In addition to the word "cattle" there are mentioned beeves, bulls, bullocks, calves, cows, fatlings, heifers, and kine. Many different kinds of cattle were spread over the Holy Land in Biblical days. Small, black or brown, short-legged, short-horned cattle were found in the southern part of Judah. This type of cattle easily submitted to the yoke and was prominent in agricultural operations. Along the coast a larger variety was found, and the wild districts east of the Jordan River were populated with a huge, black breed of cattle. The bullock was the most prized member of the bovine family because of its importance for religious sacrifice.

The calf was also greatly valued by the Hebrews. It was used for sacrifice, was important as food, as booty, as a figure in prophecy, and was on occasion even made an object of worship. The calf was also a popular representation of the Deity among the Canaanites, the golden calf that the Hebrews set up when Moses went to receive the Ten Commandments being an example.

There are 48 references in the Bible to the calf or calves. The cow is mentioned 7 times, and its Biblical plural, kine, is mentioned 23 times. Fatlings are named 6 times and heifers are named 20 times. There are 151 references to cattle. Cattle products are also frequently mentioned in the Bible. Milk is mentioned 48 times, butter 11 times, and cheese 3 times.

Subfamily *Hippotraginae*

The great family *Bovidae* is divided into a number of subfamilies. In addition to the True Oxen (*Bovinae*), there are the Deer-Oxen (*Boselaphinae*), the Twist-horned Oxen or Antelopes, such as the Elands and Bushbucks (*Strepsicerosinae*), and seven others. One of these is the *Hippotraginae* or, literally, "The Horse-Antelopes" which includes the addax, oryx, and sable antelope. They have hairy muzzles and ringed, backward-curving horns in both male and female.

12. Bubal (Hartebeest)

The Hebrew word *yahmur*, which is used twice in the Bible, both times describing a beast that could be eaten, has puzzled scholars for many years. Modern commentators generally agree that the animal referred to is the Bubal, a rare antelope of North Africa which is a species of hartebeest.

The Bubal was well known to the ancients. They described it, rather accurately, as a cross between a calf and a stag, which, with its thick body, short horns, and drawn-out head, it indeed looks like. It was considered to be a wild cow, thus separating it from the several species of antelope known to the Hebrews. Actually, this classification is a misrepresentation, for despite its strange appearance the Bubal is a fullfledged antelope.

The two mentions of the Bubal are in Deuteronomy (14:5), where it is listed among the hooved animals that could be eaten under the Mosaic law, and in I Kings (4:23) where it is mentioned as having graced the table of Solomon. Many versions of the Bible still use other translations for the word, such as "wild cow" and so on. It is quite likely, though, that the writer of the Bible was not so vague—that he had a specific animal in mind, and probably that animal was the Bubal.

13. Addax Antelope (Pygarg)

"These *are* the beasts which ye shall eat: the ox, the sheep, and the goat, The hart, and the roebuck, and the fallow deer, and the wild goat, and the pygarg, and the wild ox, and the chamois" (Deut. 14:4–5).

The Pygarg is named in the Bible as one of the clean beasts which could be eaten by the Israelites. The Hebrew word that was translated as "pygarg" is *dishon*, which was left untranslated in the Jewish Bible. However, its literal meaning is either "trader" or "leaper." The *Septuagint*, the Greek translation of the Bible, translated *dishon* as "pygargos." The first English translators used the word "pygarg" in their version.

"Pygarg" has the literal meaning of "white-crouped," and many scholars have therefore felt that the animal intended was a white-rumped
antelope because *"croup(e)"* in Old English meant "rump." The most
common white-rumped antelope of that day would probably have been
the Addax. This graceful animal inhabited North Africa but its range extended into western Asia. Certainly it would have been a familiar animal
in Palestine, for it can still be found there in considerable numbers.

It was probably hunted by the same method used to hunt wild
bulls: the animal would be chased into a net, and then camouflaged
hunters would spring from their hiding places and kill it.

Several persons in the Old Testament had names that were the
same as this animal's, or were obviously derived from it. Both *Dishon*
and *Dishan* appear often in the Old Testament as proper names. Three
of the dukes of Edom, who were descendants of Esau, had these names.

14. Oryx (Wild Bull, Wild Ox)

"Thy sons have fainted, they lie at the head of all the streets, as a wild
bull in a net: they are full of the fury of the Lord, the rebuke of thy
God" (Isa. 51:20).

The Hebrew word *teô* is found twice in the Bible, once being translated as "wild bull" and the other time as "wild ox." The Jewish Bible
preserves these renderings, thus affirming the ambiguity of the word.
This is a perfect example of the type of mistranslation mentioned
earlier. The Hebrew word (*teô*) is quite distinct (from *re'em*) and definitive. The latter definitely applied to the Aurochs or true Wild Ox, though
the English translators called it the "Unicorn." Thus, the *teô* must be
another animal.

From the expression of Isaiah it is evident that this animal must
have been a strong one which demanded the use of nets in catching
it. This method of hunting was used only for the larger game. It involved stretching a rope tightly along the ground in some ravine close
to the favorite haunts of the animal being hunted. Then a net with a
smaller rope was attached along this, and allowed to droop over poles
not fixed tightly in the ground. When the animal was driven into the
net it collapsed upon him, and he became tangled within it. The waiting
hunters could then make an easy kill.

Most scholars believe that *teô* meant one of the three large antelope
species, namely the leucoryx, or, as it is more commonly called, the
White Oryx. This antelope, related to the pygarg discussed earlier, once
roamed the entire range of desert land from Persia to the Sahara. In
Biblical days, it was common throughout Palestine; but it is probably
now extinct there.

Subfamily *Gazellinae*

These are small or medium-sized hoofed animals, which are characterized by narrow teeth, hairy muzzles, and, in most species, ringed horns in both sexes.

15. *Gazelles*

The word "roe" occurs 12 times in the Bible. Eleven of these times it appears as the word *tsebi*, a Hebrew word that the English translated as "roebuck"; and once it is written *ya'alah*, the feminine form, in Hebrew (Prov. 5:19). However, scholars now seem to agree that a gazelle was the animal intended by the Biblical writers. There is real confusion concerning the identity of this animal, again due, for the most part, to the lack of zoological knowledge on the part of the European, and notably the English, translators of the Bible. An animal known as the Roedeer (*Capreolus*) is one, if not the commonest, of the deer of Europe. It is a true deer and its range today extends from Scotland to the Tien Shan and Siberia. It is a woods dweller and it is possible that it may have inhabited the northern Levant coast when that area was forested. However, there is no direct evidence of this. The Roebuck— of which the female is commonly known simply as the Doe, as for all deer—is not an antelope, or even a member of the Bovine family. However, one (possibly two) species of gazelle (*Gazella arabica*) was, in Biblical times, the commonest game animal of Palestine. Even today this species is quite common throughout the desert and steppe areas of the land.

Where the translators say "Roebuck" they mean the male gazelle and this was listed among the clean animals that could be eaten by the Israelite people. The doe was omitted both from the lists of clean animals and the lists of meat served at Solomon's feast. The roebuck, on the other hand, is specifically listed in both instances.

This was one of the most hunted of all game animals. Extremely fleet of foot, they were trapped by various means. They were encircled with nets, driven into enclosures with pitfalls, or forced into narrow valleys and shot with arrows. Later, falcons and greyhounds were trained to hunt them. These learned to delay the gazelles by their feints until the hunter could kill them. Sometimes falcons and greyhounds were used simultaneously.

THE SHEEP FAMILY (*Ovidae*)

The last great family of hoofed animals is that of the *Ovidae*, which means sheep. However, this is divided into two subfamilies; that of the goats (*Caprinae*) and of the sheep (*Ovinae*). There are several intermediate types, and two animals previously grouped with the gazelles— the Saiga and the Chiru—are now associated with the former as the Gazelle-Goats.

Subfamily *Ovinae*

16. *Sheep*

"And Abimelech took sheep, and oxen, and menservants, and women-servants, and gave *them* unto Abraham, and restored him Sarah his wife" (Gen. 20:14).

"And David spake unto the Lord, when he saw the angel that smote the people, and said, Lo, I have sinned, and I have done wickedly: but these sheep, what have they done? let thine hand, I pray thee, be against me, and against my father's house" (II Sam. 24:17).

"Also king Solomon, and all the congregation of Israel that were assembled unto him before the ark, sacrificed sheep and oxen, which could not be told nor numbered for multitude" (II Chron. 5:6).

"Thou madest him to have dominion over the works of thy hands: thou hast put all *things* under his feet: All sheep and oxen, yea, and the beasts of the field . . ." (Ps. 8:6–7).

"Like sheep they are laid in the grave; death shall feed on them; and the upright shall have dominion over them in the morning; and their beauty shall consume in the grave from their dwelling" (Ps. 49:14).

"Thy teeth *are* like a flock *of sheep that are even* shorn, which came up from the washing; whereof every one bear twins, and none *is* barren among them" (Song of Sol. 4:2).

Sheep occupy the largest space of any animal in the Bible. They are directly referred to, by some name such as ewe, lamb, or ram, or some fact is given concerning them, a total of 742 times. The Israelites were original sheepherders of these steppes. Further, the shepherds of those days could have enormous flocks of sheep because pasture was free and unlimited. The animal assumed a vital role in Hebrew culture, bound up indivisibly with the religious, civil, and domestic life of the Israelites.

The flesh of sheep was a luxury in the Biblical culture. Although King Solomon required a daily provision of 100 sheep for his table, the common people ate it only on festive occasions.

A young ram was almost always chosen, for his death was not as great a loss to the future prospects of the herd as the death of a young ewe would have been. It was cooked in a huge caldron filled with water.

The principal food supplied by the sheep was its milk. An extremely rich milk, it was usually allowed to curdle before drinking. This custom still persists today, and this curdled milk is known as *leben*. Although butter was sometimes made from the milk of sheep, cow's or goat's milk was generally used for this purpose.

Since in ancient times nearly all clothing was made from wool, the value of the sheep's fleece cannot be underestimated. According to John G. Wood, "the wool of the sheep of Palestine differed extremely in value; some kinds being coarse and rough, while others were long, fine, and soft." Wool was taken from sheep of various colors, but the most valuable color was pure white. Still, sheep wool was often died various colors, blue, purple and scarlet being the most popular hues.

Even the sheep's horns were utilized. The Hebrew trumpet, called the *shofar*, which was used to announce the Feast of Trumpets, was made from the left horn of the broad-tailed sheep. Wood states that "the old Rabbinical writers have a curious saying about the ram. 'The ram in life has one tone, in death six.' This they explain in the following way. When the animal is living the only sound which it can produce is the bleat, but when it is dead it is made into musical instruments: 1. Of the horns are made trumpets; 2. Of the leg-bones are made flutes; 3. Of the large intestines are made lute-strings; 4. Of the small intestines are made harp-strings; 5. Of the skin is made the drum-head; 6. Of the wool are made the pomanders which hang between the golden bells of the High Priest's garment."

Sheep were also the fundamental animal in the religious sacrifices of the Jews. It was a lamb which was offered at the greatest of the religious feasts of the Israelites, the Passover. At this time lambs would be offered by all the people in commemoration of their escape from slavery in Egypt.

17. Aoudad

"These *are* the beasts which ye shall eat: the ox, the sheep, and the goat, The hart, and the roebuck, and the fallow deer, and the wild goat, and the pygarg, and the wild ox, and the chamois" (Deut. 14:4–5).

Chamois is not the proper translation of the Hebrew word *zemer*, used in Deuteronomy. The chamois lives in the high mountain ranges of Europe. No evidence is available to show that it ever lived in Palestine.

Most Bible scholars and naturalists today agree that the wild sheep of North Africa known as the Barbary sheep is the animal intended by the Hebrew word *zemer*. This animal is also known by its Moorish name of *aoudad*. It is related to the Big Horn, or Rocky Mountain sheep, and was apparently a familiar animal to the Israelites.

These mountain sheep lived in small flocks in rugged mountain areas in Barbary, Egypt, and Mount Sinai. They were possibly abundant in the last, in Moses' time, but they were heavily depleted by the Israelite hunters. The Bedouins also know the animal well, but it has become practically extinct in the desert areas where it used to live, east of Libya.

This particular kind of mountain sheep has massive, gracefully curving horns about 2 feet in length. Since the Israelites used horns to make trumpets for pastoral, religious, and warring purposes, no doubt they frequently used the horns of the aoudads.

Subfamily *Caprinae*

This subfamily includes all the animals commonly known as goats, as well as the tahrs, the markhors, and the tur of the Caucasus. The *Caprinae* are usually characterized by horns in both sexes. Their horns are triangular in cross section and are usually ridged or knobbed. The muzzle is narrow and hairy, the tail short and flattened.

18. Ibex

"Then Saul took three thousand chosen men out of all Israel, and went to seek David and his men upon the rocks of the wild goats" (I Sam. 24:2).

"Knowest thou the time when the wild goats of the rock bring forth? *or* canst thou mark when the hinds do calve?" (Job 39:1).

"The high hills *are* a refuge for the wild goats, *and* the rocks for the conies" (Ps. 104:18).

The words "wild goat" are used four times in the Bible to translate two Hebrew words: *ako* and *azelim*. But *azelah*, a variant of the word *azelim*, was mistranslated as "roe" (Prov. 5:19) in the King James First Version.

Azelim meant literally "the climber," and therefore it would be logical to assume that the animal intended by this name was a climbing one. Almost all naturalists are convinced that the animal intended was an ibex, or the *Beden* of the Arabs.

The Beden lived in small herds of eight or ten. They can still be found in Palestine, in such areas as the weird-looking En-gedi, known as the "Fountain of the Goats." The Bible scholar Henry B. Tristram suggested that David and his followers, while outlaws, lived at En-gedi for a period of time in order to capture wild goats for food.

The flesh of the wild goat is excellent; far superior to the dry meat of the gazelle. The problem lies in catching one. Beden are extremely wary creatures and take refuge high in the craggy mountains when they are pursued.

Several proper names in the Bible are derived from the meaning of wild goat. They are Aran (wild goat), Jaala (wild she-goat), and Jael (mountain goat). Jael was the woman who killed Sisera, leader of the Canaanites, by nailing his head to her tent floor.

19. Goats

"Go now to the flock, and fetch me from thence two good kids of the goats: and I will make them savoury meat for thy father, such as he loveth . . ." (Gen. 27:9).

"These *are* the beasts which ye shall eat: the ox, the sheep, and the goat . . ." (Deut. 14:4).

"And Michal took an image, and laid *it* in the bed, and put a pillow of goats' *hair* for his bolster, and covered *it* with a cloth" (I Sam. 19:13).

"The lambs *are* for thy clothing, and the goats *are* the price of the field; And *thou shalt have* goats' milk enough for thy food, for the food of thy household, and *for* the maintenance for thy maidens" (Prov. 27:26-27).

"If thou know not, O thou fairest among women, go thy way forth by the footsteps of the flock, and feed thy kids beside the shepherds' tents" (Song of Sol. 1:8).

"Behold, thou *art* fair, my love; behold, thou *art* fair; thou *hast* doves' eyes within thy locks: thy hair *is* as a flock of goats that appear from mount Gilead" (Song of Sol. 4:1).

The writers of the Sacred Scripture spoke more often of the sheep than the goat (*Capra hirca*) but were very well acquainted with the latter.

The word "goat" appears 136 times in the Bible, and the word "kid" 51 times. Also, 11 direct references are made to the milk, hair, and skin of the goat.

The goat was a very necessary animal to the Hebrews. Since goats survive far better than animals like sheep in rocky, craggy land, they were particularly valuable animals to raise on rough terrain in the Holy Land. Almost every part of the goat's body was utilized in some beneficial way. The whole goat would be used for religious sacrifice, its flesh for food, its milk for drinking, its hair for cloth, its hide for leather, water bags, and even clothing, and its horns for trumpets.

The goat is mentioned in Dan. 8:5 as the symbol of the Macedonian empire. The silver drachmas and tetradrams of the Hellenistic kingdoms often depicted, on the obverse, the head of Alexander the Great wearing a ram's horn.

Goats were herded with sheep in Biblical days, but each group remained separate, following its own bell-laden leader. The Bible uses this herding habit symbolically, referring to the good people as the group of sheep, and to the evil as the goats. This does not mean that the goat was of inferior value to the Israelites. The goat was more generally used as food than the sheep, even though its meat was drier.

Adult male goats could not be eaten because of their strong flavor and toughness, and also because they were necessary to insure the flock's increase. But the young kid was usually the chief meat for a feast, and it would be offered to any visiting stranger as a symbol of Israelite hospitality. Goats also provided extremely good milk. It was richer than the milk of both cows and sheep, and apparently had broader uses.

The average Hebrew family could have lived almost entirely on a single goat's products. A good goat gives 3 quarts of milk a day from which a rich butter and buttermilk can be made. In Biblical days the milkmen would drive their goats from door to door to be milked by families who did not own a goat. This custom has been retained in some parts of the Holy Land even to the present.

Goatskins were important in the construction of Hebrew musical instruments. The *nebal*, a large harp, was made with goatskin for its sounding base, and drums had goatskin coverings.

THE CARNIVORES (Order, *Carnivora*)

In the Order *Carnivora* scientists have grouped an extensive array of animals including the cats, civets, bears, dogs, hyenas, raccoons, and weasels, together with their aquatic cousins, the walruses, sea lions, and seals. Probably the most distinctive Carnivore characteristic is that members of the order subsist mainly on the flesh of other animals which they track down and kill. Although this is generally the case, there are exceptions. Bears, for example, augment their diet with fruits, berries, honey, and even insects. In line with their general flesh-eating habits, most Carnivores have large, well-developed teeth that have sharp cutting edges. The canines are usually long and well adapted for seizing and holding prey. There are never less than four functional toes and frequently they number five. In all cases the toes are equipped with sharp, curved claws that have no resemblance to the hoofs of the Ungulates.

THE CAT FAMILY (*Felidae*)

Including lions, leopards, tigers, pumas, jaguars, and lynxes, as well as the domestic cats, the *Felidae* are Carnivores par excellence. Their long, powerful bodies are well adapted for killing prey much larger than themselves. They are differentiated from other members of the order by having a short muzzle and a reduced number of teeth. The canines and flesh teeth are well developed. Another distinctive characteristic of this family is that their sharp, strongly curved claws are retractile and can be withdrawn into protective sheaths. Their tongues are furnished with a number of flat, stiff processes, called papillae, which point backward and enable the organ to be used as an effective rasp, both for licking meat from bones and for cleaning their heavy fur. Fringing the muzzle are a series of long whiskers provided at their bases with special nerves. These act as an extra set of sense organs that help the cats find their way about at night.

20. Lion

"Judah *is* a lion's whelp; from the prey, my son, thou art gone up: he stooped down, he couched as a lion, and as an old lion; who shall rouse him up?" (Gen. 49:9).

"And after a time he returned to take her, and he turned aside to see the carcase of the lion; and, behold, *there was* a swarm of bees and honey in the carcase of the lion" (Judg. 14:8).

"The roaring of the lion, and the voice of the fierce lion, and the teeth of the young lions, are broken. The old lion perisheth for lack of prey, and the stout lion's whelps are scattered abroad" (Job 4:10–11).

"The young lions roar after their prey, and seek their meat from God" (Ps. 104:21).

"The burden of the beasts of the south: into the land of trouble and anguish, from whence *come* the young and old lion, the viper and fiery flying serpent, they will carry their riches upon the shoulders of young asses, and their treasures upon the bunches of camels, to a people *that* shall not profit *them*" (Isa. 30:6).

"And she brought up one of her whelps: it became a young lion, and it learned to catch the prey; it devoured men" (Ezek. 19:3).

The lion is mentioned in the Bible more often than any other undomesticated animal. It is named 157 times in 31 of the 66 books of the Bible. Lions are treated in the Bible both as natural animals and as symbols of power and strength. The lion was the ensign of the tribe of Judah, and was used by Solomon in the decoration of his house and temple.

The lion found in Biblical days in Palestine was indigenous and was described by Pliny and Aristotle, and was carved on the Assyrian monuments. The Bible records several instances where men killed them singlehanded.

According to the Bible, the mountains of Lebanon in northern Palestine provided a naturally safe home for lions (Song of Sol. 4:8, Isa. 30:6). In addition to these natural dens, lions also lived in artificial pits maintained by Oriental monarchs as places of execution (Ezek. 19:1–9, Dan. 6:7–16). These lions were caught in camouflaged nets or pits. In Bible times, they were not pitted against each other or against gladiators, as was the later practice of the Romans.

It is interesting to note the different Biblical names that derive from the words for lion. The following are examples: Ahasuerus (lion-king), Ara (lion), Arieh (lion), Ariel (lion of God), Laish (lion), Arisai (lion-like), Lebaoth (lionesses), Beth-lebaoth (house of lionesses), the cult of Nergal (lion), and Othni (lion of God, powerful).

21. *Leopard*

"Come with me from Lebanon, *my* spouse, with me from Lebanon: look from the top of Amana, from the top of Shenir and Hermon, from the lions' dens, from the mountains of the leopards" (Song of Sol. 4:8).

"The wolf also shall dwell with the lamb, and the leopard shall lie down with the kid; and the calf, and the young lion, and the fatling together; and a little child shall lead them" (Isa. 11:6).

"Can the Ethiopian change his skin, or the leopard his spots? *then* may ye also do good, that are accustomed to do evil" (Jer. 13:23).

"After this I beheld, and, lo, another, like a leopard, which had upon the back of it four wings of a fowl; the beast had also four heads; and dominion was given to it" (Dan. 7:6).

"Therefore I will be unto them as a lion; as a leopard by the way will I observe *them* . . ." (Hos. 13:7).

"Their horses also are swifter than the leopards, and are more fierce than the evening wolves: and their horsemen shall spread themselves, and their horsemen shall come from far; they shall fly as the eagle *that* hasteth to eat" (Hab. 1:8).

The leopard is mentioned only 8 times in Scripture, and in only 2 of these places is the animal literally signified. Despite this brevity, the Bible so clearly delineates the attributes of the leopard it cannot be doubted that the animal was well known in Palestine. Its ferocity, color, craft, swiftness, and dwelling place are all touched upon in the few, short references. The craftiness of the leopard as a truly predaceous creature is alluded to more than once in the Bible. The Israelite shepherds were terrified of this animal, for it constantly ravaged their sheep and goats. With its stealth and cunning, the leopard was adept at stalking a stray goat or sheep over the most rough terrain. In this respect it was even more dangerous than the lion, which would only attack herds and which customarily proclaims itself loudly when hunting.

The peculiar localities loved by the leopard are mentioned in the Song of Solomon. It dwelt almost exclusively in the large forests of pine, oak, and cedar which covered the mountains of Lebanon. The few leopards that remain in Palestine today are found in the remote regions of Mount Tabor and Mount Carmel.

Several Biblical names are derived from *namer*, the word for leopard. Nimrah (leopardess) was the name of a fenced city; Beth-Nimrah (house of leopardess) was a variant of the same name; and Nimrim (leopards) was the name of a district northeast of the Dead Sea.

22. Cat

The word "cat" is not mentioned in the whole of the canonical Scriptures and only once in the Apocrypha. The one reference occurs in the Book of Baruch, in which the gods of Babylon are denounced as false gods "of silver and of gold, and of wood . . . They are as one of the beams of the temple, yet they say their hearts are gnawed upon by things creeping out of the earth; and when they eat them and their clothes they feel it not. Their faces are blacked through the smoke that cometh out of the temple. Upon their bodies and heads sit bats, swallows, and birds, and the cats also. By this ye may know that they are not gods; therefore fear them not."

The passage is not very complimentary to cats, but perhaps it explains why the animals were confined to noncanonical works. The scene of the passage is Jerusalem at the beginning of the seventh century B.C., shortly after the Babylonian king, Nebuchadnezzar II, had crushed the Jewish rebellion, destroyed the city, and carried the leading Jews into exile. Chapter 6:22 from the Book of Baruch, from which the passage is taken, is the epistle which Jeremy "sent unto them which were to be led captives unto Babylon by the king of the Babylonians to certify them, as it was commanded him of God."

Thus, the Israelites, whose tribes had formerly been enslaved by the Egyptians, a cat-worshiping people, found that their latest tormentors, the Babylonians, also kept cats in their temples. It is no wonder, then, that the Israelites chose to leave the little beasts out of the Sacred Scripture of the Old Testament, and mentioned them in so uncomplimentary a fashion in the Apocrypha.

THE BEAR FAMILY (*Ursidae*)

The bears constitute a unique group of Carnivores that closely resemble one another in body form. They are characterized by a heavy, massive build, with thick limbs and short tails. Their five-toed feet are armed with powerful, nonretractile claws well suited for digging. Unlike the other Carnivores, bears possess cheek-teeth with nearly flat crowns that they use for grinding vegetation and insects. In most cases the fur is coarse, long, and shaggy, and some shade of brown.

23. Bear

"And David said unto Saul, Thy servant kept his father's sheep, and there came a lion, and a bear, and took a lamb out of the flock; And I went out after him, and smote him, and delivered *it* out of his mouth: and when he arose against me, I caught *him* by his beard, and smote him, and slew him. Thy servant slew both the lion and the bear; and this uncircumcised Philistine shall be as one of them, seeing he hath defied the armies of the living God" (I Sam. 17:34-36).

"And he turned back, and looked on them, and cursed them in the name of the Lord. And there came forth two she bears out of the wood, and tare forty and two children of them" (II Kings 2:24).

"Let a bear robbed of her whelps meet a man, rather than a fool in his folly" (Prov. 17:12).

"*As* a roaring lion, and a ranging bear; *so is* a wicked ruler over the poor people" (Prov. 28:15).

"We roar all like bears, and mourn sore like doves: we look for judgment, but *there is* none; for salvation, *but* it is far off from us" (Isa. 59:11).

"And behold another beast, a second, like to a bear, and it raised up itself on one side, and it had three ribs in the mouth of it between the teeth of it: and they said thus unto it, Arise, devour much flesh"

The bear is portrayed in the Bible as a dangerous animal. Often it is coupled with the lion as one of the two animals to avoid at all costs. According to the Bible, the most dangerous bear is the mother bereft of her cubs. The Hebrew word for the mother bear who has lost her cubs literally meant "bereaved." Such a mother will attempt anything to recover her cubs, and is indeed a fearsome foe.

Bears were quite plentiful in Palestine in early days before the advent of modern weapons and the destruction of forests. But today they are much more limited in number, being confined to the regions of Lebanon and Anti-Lebanon north of Palestine. Many lived along the steep walls of the canyon in which the river Leontes flows to the Mediterranean Sea above Tyre. The color of the Palestinian bear varied from dark brown as a cub, to yellowish brown as an adult, to dirty white in old age.

In the book of Job reference is made to "Arcturus with his sons." Arcturus, meaning bear-guard or bear-keeper, is a fixed star of the first magnitude in the constellation Boötes. It is popularly conceived as representing the constellation Ursa Major, which is known as the Great Bear. The North Star is in Ursa Minor, known as the Little Bear, and is in line with the Great Bear. Thus "Arcturus with his sons" probably refers to the sky-bear with his star-train, the sons being the three stars that form his tail.

THE DOG FAMILY (*Canidae*)

Together with the domestic dogs, the *Canidae* includes wolves, foxes, jackals, the Cape hunting dog, and wild dogs or dholes. They constitute a well-defined group, the wild members of which cannot be confused with any other group. All are characterized by long, pointed muzzles, moderately long tails, and feet furnished with blunt, nonretractile claws. With the exception of the Cape hunting dog, all wild members of the family exhibit a more or less uniform, somber coloration which varies from gray to a yellowish or reddish brown. The sense of smell is highly developed and acts as an aid in hunting. The *Canidae* differ markedly from the cats in that they tend to live and hunt in packs rather than singly. Most members subsist solely on flesh; some eat lizards, mice, snails, and even insects, while the jackals live largely on carrion.

24. Wolf

"Benjamin shall ravin *as* a wolf; in the morning he shall devour the prey, and at night he shall divide the spoil" (Gen. 49:27).

"Wherefore a lion out of the forest shall slay them, *and* a wolf of the evenings shall spoil them, a leopard shall watch over their cities: every one that goeth out thence shall be torn in pieces; because their transgressions are many, *and* their backslidings are increased" (Jer. 5:6).

"Her princes in the midst thereof *are* like wolves ravening the prey, to shed blood, *and* to destroy souls, to get dishonest gain" (Ezek. 22:27).

"Their horses also are swifter than the leopards, and are more fierce than the evening wolves: and their horsemen shall spread themselves, and their horsemen shall come from far; they shall fly as the eagle *that* hasteth to eat" (Hab. 1:8).

"Her princes within her *are* roaring lions; her judges *are* evening wolves; they gnaw not the bones till the morrow" (Zeph. 3:3).

"Beware of false prophets, which come to you in sheep's clothing, but inwardly they are ravening wolves" (Matt. 7:15).

The Hebrew word *zeeb* and the Greek word *lykos* are rightly translated as "wolf" in the Bible, although all references are made metaphorically without any wolf ever actually being mentioned.

In 12 verses wolves are named 30 times. The name is used as a symbol of a treacherous enemy. Never does a Biblical writer mention an act performed by a wolf. Unlike other beasts of prey, such as the lion and bear, there are no instances recorded in the Bible of a wolf attacking either animals or men.

Individually, the wolf is a rather timid animal—it would much rather avoid a man than encounter him. But collectively the wolf can be one of the most dangerous animals alive. Swiftness of foot avails nothing against a wolf pack's pursuit, because the animals can maintain their long, loping gallop for hours at a time.

Proper names derived from the wolf appear frequently in the Bible.

For example, Zeeb was the name of a Midianite chieftain, and Lycaonia, the name of a village in Asia Minor, apparently derived from *lykos* (the Greek word for wolf).

25. Dog

"But against any of the children of Israel shall not a dog move his tongue, against man or beast; that ye may know how that the Lord doth put a difference between the Egyptians and Israel" (Exod. 11:7).

"Thou shalt not bring the hire of a whore, or the price of a dog, into the house of the Lord thy God for any vow: for even both these *are* abomination unto the Lord thy God" (Deut. 23:18).

"And the Philistine said unto David, *Am* I a dog, that thou comest to me with staves? And the Philistine cursed David by his gods" (I Sam. 17:43).

"After whom is the king of Israel come out? after whom dost thou pursue? after a dead dog, after a flea" (I Sam. 24:14).

"But now *they that are* younger than I have me in derision, whose fathers I would have disdained to have set with the dogs of my flock" (Job 30:1).

"And at evening let them return, *and* let them make a noise like a dog, and go round about the city" (Ps. 59:14).

"There be three *things* which go well, yea, four are comely in going: A lion *which is* strongest among beasts, and turneth not away for any; A greyhound; an he goat also; and a king, against whom *there is* no rising up" (Prov. 30:29–31).

The dog is referred to 41 times in the Bible, and almost without exception with strong disfavor. This attitude is common among all Near Eastern people, and it persists even today. It is difficult for us in the Western world, where the dog is one of the most cherished of all animals, to understand this attitude toward dogs.

The disapproval of dogs by the Israelites probably stemmed from the fact that packs of dogs ran wild through the streets of all Near and Middle Eastern cities, including those of Palestine. They would run through the streets at night howling, hungry, and snarling, after having slept all day. They were considered cowardly, filthy creatures; to call a Hebrew a dog was one of the most terrible insults possible; however, if the Hebrew called himself a dog, it was considered a display of the deepest humility.

The Israelites did not consider dogs completely useless, for there is some Scriptural evidence that they were used to guard the flocks (Job 30:1). Dogs are spoken of figuratively throughout the Bible. Solomon makes reference to them in his proverbs. ("As a dog returneth to his vomit, *so* a fool returneth to his folly"—Prov. 26:11.) In the Book of Isaiah the lax priests of that day were compared to dumb dogs.

It seems as though the dogs spoken of in Scripture are more like their cousins, the wolves and jackals, than the domesticated animals we know today. Apparently packs of dogs would often attack the Israelite people, and sometimes even ravaged freshly buried corpses.

Today in Palestine and the East the dog is still regarded with the general contempt accorded it in Biblical times. Arabs refer to Christians as "dogs," as the Jews once did to the Gentiles. Packs of half wild pariah dogs still roam the streets and countryside in many areas, although their number is fast decreasing.

Though usually considered mongrel, the pariah dog is, in fact, a rather well-defined form of *Canis familiaris* and has remained relatively pure bred. These packs are very interesting scientifically, for they enable us to study the canine type in a semiwild state. In the Near East most of the research on the pariah dog has been carried out by Drs. R. and R. Menzel of Israel. They have shown the dogs to be of medium size, and to vary in head and body shape from the sheepdog type to a greyhound type. In behavior it has been found that these animals occupy the full range between absolute wildness and full domestication. Any animal, regardless of its place by birth within this range, can adapt itself to a changing environment, either toward wildness or domestication. Drs. Menzel tamed a number of wild pariahs which, later, could not be distinguished from animals born in captivity.

The word "greyhound" occurs only once in the Bible, and it is questionable whether this is really the proper way of translating the Hebrew word *zar-zir-mathmain*. Bible scholars have varied greatly in their ideas as to the best translation of this Hebrew word. The literal meaning of it is "one with the loins well girded." Thus most critics have thought an animal sleek and comely in appearance was intended. Some of the suggested meanings besides the greyhound have been the zebra, the leopard, the horse, a proud cock, and the starling. Some have even suggested that a human athlete or warrior was intended!

Such a problem as this will probably never be fully resolved. However, "greyhound" remains a good translation, for it is certainly a beautiful, graceful animal that deserves to be spoken of as "comely in going." Also no doubt it was a dog that was familiar to the Israelites, since it was among the first varieties of dogs known to man. It was a favorite of the Egyptians and has been found etched upon some of their ancient monuments, commemorating the sport of hunting. Greyhounds were kept by the Egyptians in huge kennel systems because of their value in hunting wild animals. The greyhounds would also accompany their aristocratic masters on inspection tours for the purpose of determining the efficiency of the slaves' work output.

The Israelites would also have been familiar with the greyhound from another source. The Assyrians, who lived northeast of Palestine, also honored the greyhound. Proof of this is evident in their monuments. Solomon, who wrote the proverb which speaks of four comely things, was a man of wide knowledge, and may well have intended to use an animal revered far and wide such as the greyhound as one of his examples of comeliness.

26. Jackals

The jackal is frequently alluded to in Scripture, though its name appears in no Western translation due to the fact that the animal does not exist in Europe and was unknown to the translators. "Fox" is regularly substituted. The jackal seems to be designated by several Hebrew names:

iyyim—the howlers (translated as "fawn" in the Douay Version)

tan—the stretcher

than—denizen of desolate places (often wrongly translated as dragon!)

There are numerous Biblical references to the howling and gregariousness of jackals.

27. Fox

"And Samson went and caught three hundred foxes, and took firebrands, and turned tail to tail, and put a firebrand in the midst between two tails" (Judg. 15:4).

"Now Tobiah the Ammonite *was* by him, and he said, Even that which they build, if a fox go up, he shall even break down their stone wall" (Neh. 4:3).

"They shall fall by the sword; they shall be a portion for foxes" (Ps. 63:10).

"Take us the foxes, the little foxes, that spoil the vines: for our vines *have* tender grapes" (Song of Sol. 2:15).

"Because of the mountain of Zion, which is desolate, the foxes walk upon it" (Lam. 5:18).

"O Israel, thy prophets are like the foxes in the deserts" (Ezek. 13:4).

Foxes are mentioned 9 times in the Bible. The common fox found in Palestine was much like the Red Fox found in Europe and North America today. However, two additional kinds also occurred there: the Egyptian Fox, a small animal found abundantly in southern Palestine and east of the Jordan River; and the Syrian Fox, a larger animal found in the northern forests of Palestine.

The foxes had an interesting habit of living in the old, deserted ruins of Palestine, particularly around Mount Zion and Jerusalem. Although foxes are treated in the Bible with contempt, they are considered very clever and cunning animals.

THE HYENA FAMILY (*Hyaenidae*)

The hyenas are massively built animals, with the fore-legs longer than the hind-legs. The coarse, shaggy fur is marked with either vertical stripes or blackish spots. Both fore- and hind-feet have four toes equipped with strong claws similar to those of dogs. The molar teeth of hyenas resemble those of cats, but the premolars are unique. Tall and nearly conical, they are set in jaws that are probably more powerful than those of any other Carnivore. Hyenas can crush the shinbone of an ox as easily as a dog can crush the bones of a chicken.

28. Hyena

"And another company turned the way *to* Beth-horon: and another company turned *to* the way of the border that looketh to the valley of Zeboim toward the wilderness" (I Sam. 13:18).

"Mine heritage *is* unto me *as* a speckled bird; the birds round about *are* against her; come ye, assemble all the beasts of the field, come to devour" (Jer. 12:9).

Although no English translations of the Bible include the word "hyena," it is evident that two passages in the Old Testament refer to that animal. The Hebrew word *zabua,* meaning "something streaked," is rendered "hyena" in the Septuagint, the Greek version of the Bible. Most scholars agree that rather than a speckled bird (Jer. 12:9), this was the animal intended.

The Striped Hyaena was plentiful in ancient Egypt and was often depicted on their monuments. It was then also found in parts of Persia, Syria, India, and Arabia. In Palestine it was once extremely abundant, and even today a few apparently remain there.

Many superstitions prevailed among the Israelites concerning the hyena. For example, when one was killed its hide was stripped away, tanned in the Dead Sea, made into leggings and sandals, and worn as a magical charm to defend the wearer against the hyena's bite. The Israelites would also take the carcass of a hyena to leeward from the tents before stripping off the skin, because they believed a dead hyena's scent would corrupt the air. A further superstition found in Palestine was that if a hyena met a solitary man at night, it could charm him in such a manner that he would be its unresisting prey. But if another person were present this power of the hyena would be absent. This superstition was so strong that the Palestinians always demanded company for their night journeys.

Since the hyenas were notorious for raiding the graves of the dead, all Israelites who could afford it arranged for burial in tombs protected by massive stone doors. Absalom, the son of David who was killed by Joab, was buried under a huge pile of stones to protect his corpse from the attacks of hyenas.

THE WEASEL FAMILY (*Mustelidae*)

The Family *Mustelidae* includes a number of related animals that often differ markedly in external characteristics. Among the members of the group are the weasels, badgers, otters, martens, mink, skunks, and wolverines. *Mustelidae* are characterized by their rather elongated bodies and short limbs. Most are of medium or small size. None are large, and one can slip through a hole the size of a quarter. In all cases the feet have five toes. Many members of the family are clothed with furs of great brilliance and beauty that are of high commercial value.

29. Weasel

"These also *shall be* unclean unto you among the creeping things that creep upon the earth; the weasel, and the mouse, and the tortoise after his kind . . ." (Lev. 11:29).

The word "weasel" occurs only once in the Bible, and since there is nothing in the context to define the appearance or habits of the animal, there is considerable controversy as to its identification. The passage in which it is named (see above) is a listing of animals that are unclean for eating purposes. Since weasels were apparently plentiful in Palestine during Biblical days, it could easily have been the particular animal intended by the Hebrew word *choled*. The Septuagint favors this translation. It could be, however, that a variety of other animals was meant. Such an animal as the Ichneumon or Mongoose may have been included within the meaning of *choled*.

The proper name Huldah definitely meant weasel, and this was the name of the prophetess who was consulted by King Josiah when Hilkiah found the Book of the Law (II Kings 22:14, II Chron. 34:22).

30. Badger

"And this *is* the offering which ye shall take of them; gold, and silver, and brass, And blue, and purple, and scarlet, and fine linen, and goats' *hair*, And rams' skins dyed red, and badgers' skins, and shittim wood . . ." (Exod. 25:3–5).

"And he made a covering for the tent *of* rams' skins dyed red, and a covering *of* badgers' skins above *that*" (Exod. 36:19).

"And they brought the tabernacle unto Moses, the tent, and all his furniture, his taches, his boards, his bars, and his pillars, and his sockets, And the covering of rams' skins dyed red, and the covering of badgers' skins, and the vail of the covering . . ." (Exod. 39:33–34).

"And when the camp setteth forward, Aaron shall come, and his sons, and they shall take down the covering vail, and cover the ark of testimony with it; And shall put thereon the covering of badgers' skins, and shall spread over *it* a cloth wholly of blue, and shall put in the staves thereof" (Num. 4:5–6).

"And they shall bear the curtains of the tabernacle, and the tabernacle of the congregation, his covering, and the covering of the badgers' skins that *is* above upon it, and the hanging for the door of the tabernacle of the congregation" (Num. 4:25).

"I clothed thee also with broidered work, and shod thee with badgers' skin, and I girded thee about with fine linen, and I covered thee with silk" (Ezek. 16:10).

It is apparent from the Scriptural references that the badger's value in Biblical days lay in the use of its skin as a covering for tents. Its skin is mentioned 14 times in the Bible as being a useful covering for tents. Yet, the Hebrew name *takhash* is regarded by various writers as meaning a dolphin, seal, or dugong of the Red Sea! (There is no seal indigenous to the Red Sea.)

Badger skins were particularly used as the outermost covering of the Israelites' tabernacle. Since this covering would probably stretch over the entire structure, this would necessitate this badger-skin covering being 75 feet long and 45 feet wide.

Badger skins were also used to cover the tabernacle furniture when it was being carried. In fact, badger skins were listed along with gold, jewels, scarlet-dyed rams' skins, and rare shittim woods as the costliest articles for religious offerings.

THE MONKEY ORDER (Order, *Primates*)

As a group, the Primates contain some of the most highly specialized forms of animal life. Although the Order of Primates includes such diverse creatures as man, apes, monkeys, lemurs, and tarsiers, there are certain characteristics that are found in most, if not all, of the members. Generally speaking, there are always five digits on the feet, and the relation of the first digit to the other four represents one of the most important peculiarities of the group. In most cases the first digit is placed so that it opposes the others, thus transforming the feet into "hands," which serve as efficient grasping and holding organs so that the apes can be said to be four-handed. The opposable feature of the first digit has been lost in the human foot, thereby reducing man to a two-handed status. Some of the most advanced Primates have developed the ability to rise up on their hind legs and walk in an upright position. In keeping with their herbivorous habits, the cheek-teeth of the higher Primates have broad, flattened crowns that are adapted for grinding.

31. Ape

"For the king had at sea a navy of Tharshish with the navy of Hiram: once in three years came the navy of Tharshish, bringing gold, and silver, ivory, and apes, and peacocks" (I Kings 10:22).

"For the king's ships went to Tarshish with the servants of Huram: every three years once came the ships of Tarshish bringing gold, and silver, ivory, and apes, and peacocks" (II Chron. 9:21).

The word "ape" appears only twice in the Bible. In both instances it is in connection with King Solomon's collection of wealth. Apparently apes were part of the treasure collected for the king's court from southern India and Ceylon by the ships which went southward through the Red Sea and then eastward into the Indian Ocean. Other monkeys may also have been brought from Abyssinia.

The belief that Solomon's treasures came from India and Ceylon was strongly substantiated by Sir James Emerson Tennent, a British author, who pointed out that in the Tamil language spoken in both these countries the names for apes, ivory, and peacocks are identical with the Hebrew names. This seems to indicate that the Hebrews imported the names along with the other treasures.

The kind of monkeys secured for Solomon is not certain, but they most probably were not an Eastern species of *ape*, such as a gibbon or orangutan. More likely they were Indian monkeys such as a rhesus, the Wanderoo or langur. *Kophim*, the Hebrew word for "apes," is a general term which applies to all simians. Therefore both monkeys and apes, tailed and tailless, could be referred to in the Bible by the single word *kophim*.

Neither monkeys nor apes were native to the Biblical lands, but no doubt the Israelites had been made aware of the creatures quite early, for the nearby Egyptians prized several kinds of monkeys, notably the Hamadryas baboon, which they trained.

In Egypt, this baboon was considered sacred to the god Thoth. The male of the species was revered primarily in the temples, while the more docile female was often kept as a house pet. Quite often these pet baboons had some of their teeth removed or ground down, as in the case of one belonging to Thothmes III, in order to lessen the danger of their bite. That these creatures were highly prized by their owners is evident from the fact that quite often they were mummified and buried with great honors. It is interesting to note that examination of these mummies has revealed that they frequently suffered from the crippling diseases of rickets, tumors, and tubercular rheumatism.

The Israelites were probably also familiar with the Barbary apes of North Africa, and with the African true baboons, which the Biblical scholar Tristram believed was the species referred to by the term "satyr" in Isa. 13:21, 34:14.

THE BAT ORDER (Order, *Chiroptera*)

The bats are the only group of mammals ever to attain the power of true flight. In order to facilitate this, the fore-limbs display a unique construction. The bone of the upper arm is only moderately extended but the fore-arm is considerably elongated with one of its bones (the ulna) two thirds atrophied and fused with the other (the radius). With the exception of the thumb, the bones of the hand form long, slender rods which support the delicate membrane constituting the soft part of the wing. The thumb is free and terminates in a single, hooked claw that is used for climbing and hanging. The hind-feet have five toes all pointing the same way. In many forms the hind limbs are connected to the tail by a membrane similar to that of the wing. The chest of the bat is large, to accommodate the powerful muscles needed for flying. In most species the sense of hearing is very well developed. The creatures are able to fly in close quarters in total darkness by using the echo of their high-pitched squeaks as a sort of sonar.

32. Bats

"And these *are they which* ye shall have in abomination among the fowls; they shall not be eaten, they *are* an abomination; the eagle, and the ossifrage, and the ospray . . . And the stork, the heron after her kind, and the lapwing, and the bat. All fowls that creep, going upon *all* four, *shall be* an abomination unto you" (Lev. 11:13, 19–20).

"But these *are they* of which ye shall not eat: the eagle, and the ossifrage, and the ospray . . . And the stork, and the heron after her kind, and the lapwing, and the bat. And every creeping thing that flieth *is* unclean unto you: they shall not be eaten" (Deut. 14:12, 18–19).

"In that day a man shall cast his idols of silver, and his idols of gold, which they made *each one* for himself to worship, to the moles, and to the bats . . ." (Isa. 2:20).

The Hebrew word for bat, like its Greek and Latin counterparts, means "night flyer." However, the Arabic word for bat means "weak-sighted," since most bats have great difficulty seeing in the light. Even though the bat is a mammal (not a bird), the Hebrew word for fowl is still applicable to it, since the word means "winged."

Many species of bats are found in the Holy Land. Most of them are of insectivorous varieties, and sleep in caves during the day and fly for food at night. Fourteen species exist today in Palestine. They vary in size from that of a mouse to one the size of a rat which measures more than 20 inches across the wings.

Bats are classified in the Bible as unclean "birds" which should not be eaten by man, but some real birds, such as the eagle, owl, heron, stork, and swan are also included in this class of scavengers which feed on flesh and carrion.

THE GNAWING MAMMALS (Order, *Rodentia*)

Grouped under the title of rodents is a large assemblage of small- to medium-sized animals whose chief characteristic is their habit of gnawing. In all members of the Order, such as rats, porcupines, beaver, and squirrels, the incisors are of great length and are curved to form a segment of a circle; they grow throughout life. In most cases, enamel is limited to the outer edge of the incisors. Since, in the process of gnawing, the top and bottom incisors rub against each other, their size is kept constant and the edges are honed to a chisel-like edge. If one of the incisors is lost, the corresponding tooth will grow unchecked, eventually curving back, penetrating the skull, and killing the unfortunate animal. Another curious feature of many rodents is the presence of pouches in the sides of the mouth, which are used to store and carry food. Often the inner lining of the pouches is covered with soft hair. All in all, the rodents constitute a well-defined group that today is more numerous both in terms of individuals and species than any other mammalian order.

33. Mouse

"These also *shall be* unclean unto you among the creeping things that creep upon the earth; the weasel, and the mouse, and the tortoise after his kind" (Lev. 11:29).

"Then said they, What *shall be* the trespass offering which we shall return to him? They answered, Five golden emerods, and five golden mice, *according to* the number of the lords of the Philistines; for one plague *was* on you all, and on your lords" (I Sam. 6:4).

"And they laid the ark of the Lord upon the cart, and the coffer with the mice of gold and the images of their emerods" (I Sam. 6:11).

"And the golden mice, *according to* the number of all the cities of the Philistines *belonging* to the five lords, *both* of fenced cities, and of country villages, even unto the great *stone of* Abel, whereon they set down the ark of the Lord; *which stone remaineth* unto this day in the field of Joshua, the Beth-shemite" (I Sam. 6:18).

"They that sanctify themselves, and purify themselves in the gardens, behind one *tree* in the midst, eating swine's flesh, and the abomination, and the mouse, shall be consumed together, saith the Lord" (Isa. 66:17).

Mice are referred to only 6 times in the Bible. No doubt the Hebrew word *akbar* for "mouse" was a generic term that connoted several different species of tiny animals. The meaning of *akbar* is literally the "destruction of corn," so it is evident that some allusion is being made to an animal which existed in sufficient numbers to make it a formidable foe of the field crops—and therefore to rodents as a whole.

The fact that *akbar* signified a large number of different species of mice seems to indicate that its meaning included *all* the varieties found in Palestine. Tristram, the nineteenth-century Bible scholar, stated that "no less than twenty-three species of this group were ascertained by us to inhabit Palestine. Among them are three species of the dormouse *
. . . four to five species of short-tailed voles, six species of sand rats (i.e., mole-rats) and the hamster."

Some commentators translate *akbar* as "jerboa." This small animal was and still is common in Palestine. It, along with the hamster, is eaten by both the Arabs and the Syrians. Israelites in Isaiah's day apparently also ate these tiny animals, in violation of Mosaic law.

34. Mole-Rat

"These also *shall be* unclean unto you among the creeping things that creep upon the earth; the weasel, and the mouse, and the tortoise after his kind, And the ferret, and the chameleon, and the lizard, and the snail, and the mole" (Lev. 11:29-30).

"In that day a man shall cast his idols of silver, and his idols of gold, which they made *each one* for himself to worship, to the moles, and to the bats" (Isa. 2:20).

The word "mole" appears only twice in the Bible, in English. It is, however, translated from a different Hebrew word on each occasion. One of these was *tinshemeth*, and signified an unclean animal. The meaning of this word is so clouded with obscurity that scholars have despaired of ever defining it precisely. In other parts of the Bible the same word was translated as "swan," which was also an unclean food. Others have conjectured that it might have meant chameleon, salamander, land monitor, ibis, centipede, or even a true mole (*Talpa sp.*), a mammal of the Order known as the *Insectivora*.

* Dormice (*Gliridae*) are not mice, but one form—the European Hazelmouse—is mouse-sized.

The second word, *chephor-peroth*, used by Isaiah, probably referred to the mole-rat (*Spalax*), which is a rodent. This animal evidently was quite common throughout Palestine in Biblical times. It lives a subterranean life.

THE HARES, RABBITS, AND PIKAS
(Order, *Lagomorpha*)

The rabbits and the hares are distinguished by their long ears and long, powerfully developed hind-limbs. Unlike the rodents, they possess enamel on both sides of the incisor teeth. All are timid creatures that subsist primarily on vegetation. In all species, the fore-limbs have five toes and the hind-limbs have four. They breed with great rapidity, the young attaining sexual maturity 6 months after birth.

35. Hare

"Nevertheless, these shall ye not eat, of them that chew the cud, or of them that divide the hoof: *as* the camel, because he cheweth the cud, but divideth not the hoof; he *is* unclean unto you. And the coney, because he cheweth the cud, but divideth not the hoof; he *is* unclean unto you. And the hare, because he cheweth the cud, but divideth not the hoof; he *is* unclean unto you" (Lev. 11:4-6).

"Nevertheless these ye shall not eat of them that chew the cud, or of them that divide the cloven hoof; *as* the camel, and the hare, and the coney: for they chew the cud, but divide not the hoof; *therefore* they *are* unclean unto you" (Deut. 14:7).

Hares are mentioned only twice in the Bible, and both instances involve their being tabooed for eating purposes by the Mosaic law.

Their legitimacy as food was denied because they were not cloven-footed (hoof wasn't split). Moses further stated that they did, however, chew the cud. Anatomical analysis of the hare reveals that they do not re-chew their food, but Moses' error was a very natural one, for they give the appearance of rumination with their constant moving of the jaws. One commentator stated it was fortunate that the hare wasn't allowed as a food because their meat might have proved harmful due to a poisonous plant they sometimes eat. The statement is itself open to grave doubt.

Hares were quite plentiful in Palestine, and at least two species could be found. Some naturalists believe that as many as five kinds of hares ranged throughout the Holy Land. Others have thought rabbit was probably intended by the Biblical word "hare," but this seems highly unlikely, for no species of rabbit is indigenous to Palestine or surrounding countries.

THE ELEPHANTINES (Order, *Proboscidea*)

Aside from its huge size, which exceeds that of all other terrestrial mammals, the elephant's most striking characteristic is its long, flexible proboscis. This organ, with the nostrils located at its lower end, is used for grasping objects, as well as for conveying both food and water to the mouth. The males—and sometimes also the females—have large tusks in the upper jaw which correspond to one of the pairs of incisors in other mammals. In many cases these tusks grow to considerable length and are a valuable source of ivory. Elephants have short, broad feet with the toes enclosed in a common skin. Their position is indicated by broad, flat nails. The true elephant (*Elephas indicus*) inhabits India, Ceylon, and southeast Asia; in Africa there are two species of a related genus (*Loxodonta*).

36. *Elephant*

"Moreover the king made a great throne of ivory, and overlaid it with the best gold" (I Kings 10:18).

"For the king's ships went to Tarshish with the servants of Huram: every three years once came the ships of Tarshish, bringing gold, and silver, ivory, and apes, and peacocks" (II Chron. 9:21).

"All thy garments *smell* of myrrh, and aloes, *and* cassia, out of the ivory palaces, whereby they have made thee glad" (Ps. 45:8).

"His hands *are as* gold rings set with the beryl: his belly *is as* bright ivory overlaid *with* sapphires" (Song of Sol. 5:14).

"And I will smite the winter house with the summer house; and the houses of ivory shall perish, and the great houses shall have an end, saith the Lord" (Amos 3:15).

Although the elephant is never specifically mentioned in the Bible, it is directly inferred by the 9 references to ivory. In fact, some Hebrew translations of *shen-ab-biem* have marginal references to "elephants' teeth" in 2 instances where ivory is mentioned. In Job 40:15, where the word "behemoth" is used, there is also a marginal translation which states "or the elephant, as some think"; however, hippopotamus' teeth were considered better ivory than that of the elephants.

In the Bible, ivory is presented as a precious substance indeed. It is named in connection with gold, and is listed as one of the chief wonders to be seen in the palace of Solomon, who was purportedly the wealthiest monarch of his day. Apparently Solomon obtained his ivory from India and Ceylon, even though his neighbor Egypt had large treasures of ivory obtained from the African elephant. As mentioned in the section on the ape, the Hebrew names for apes, peacocks, and ivory (I Kings 10:22) are almost identical with the Singhalese language spoken in southern India and Ceylon.

In the Apocryphal books, some of which are disputed as being canonical, the elephant itself is mentioned. It is described as an engine of war, a most apt title for the role the elephant came to play in the wars that occurred in late Biblical history.

Iron chains would be wrapped around the elephant and a number of men would climb on its back; it would then be given strong wine and shown a white cloth to incite its rage; then, at the sound of a trumpet, it would charge with a terrible force which set the opposition in panic. Eventually, the vulnerable nature of the elephant's proboscis was discovered, and ingenious military men began to find ways to thwart the elephant's attack, such as cutting its tender trunk with sharp swords attached to long handles.

THE CONIES (Order, *Hyracoidea*)

The Hyraxes are small proto-ungulates that in many ways have the appearance of rodents. They differ from the rodents, however, in most features of their teeth and skeletal construction. In the upper jaw are a pair of incisors that grow throughout life in the rodent manner; instead of being chisel-like, however, they are triangular in cross section and terminate in sharp points. The number of functional toes on the fore-foot is reduced to four, of which the outermost is smaller than the others. Only three toes are present on the hind-foot. The other two hind-toes, like those of the fore-foot, have broad, short nails similar to those of the rhinoceros.

37. Coney (Hyrax)

"And the coney, because he cheweth the cud, but divideth not the hoof; he *is* unclean unto you" (Lev. 11:5).

"Nevertheless these ye shall not eat of them that chew the cud, or of them that divide the cloven hoof; *as* the camel, and the hare, and the coney: for they chew the cud, but divide not the hoof; *therefore* they *are* unclean unto you" (Deut. 14:7).

"The high hills *are* a refuge for the wild goats, *and* the rocks for the conies" (Ps. 104:18).

"There be four *things which are* little upon the earth, but they *are* exceeding wise: The ants *are* a people not strong, yet they prepare their meat in the summer; The conies *are but* a feeble folk, yet make they their houses in the rocks . . ." (Prov. 30:24–26).

The coney is mentioned only 4 times in the Bible, and twice it is in connection with the law regarding what animals should be eaten.

"Coney," or *damon* (*Hyrax syriacus*), corresponds to the Hebrew *shāphān*. This latter term has, at times, been wrongly translated as "urchin," "rabbit," and even *cherogrillus,* which is a transliteration of the Greek word for porcupine.

The hyrax lives in holes in the rocks where it can find refuge from predators, for it is comparatively defenseless. In Palestine it is often known as the "bear-rat" because of its resemblance to a vast tailless rat. Strangely enough, this little creature is related to the manatees (or sea cows), the dugongs, and the elephants. It was for some time believed by zoologists to be related to the rhinoceros.

Many people consider the flesh of coneys a delicacy, but the animals are difficult to catch. As stated in the Bible, the coneys are "exceeding wise," for they make "their houses in the rocks." The coneys are a "feeble folk," but, if cornered, will fight back and can inflict painful bites with their incisors.

The hyrax was forbidden as food to the Israelites. Its small body is clothed in soft, fine fur. The head is very like that of a vast rat: the ears are rounded and the tail almost nonexistent.

THE WHALES (Order, *Cetacea*)

Included in the Order *Cetacea* are the whales, porpoises, and dolphins, which differ from all other mammals (except the manatees and the dugong) in being fully adapted for aquatic life. Their bodies are characterized by a fishlike form; the head joins directly to the trunk with no trace of a neck, and the posterior section tapers to a forked, finlike tail arranged horizontally. The fore-limbs are present as flippers which show no outward indication of digits, and with no trace of nails or claws. There is no external indication of the hind-limbs. The thick skin is hairless, with the exception of a few bristles around the mouth of some species, and is underlaid by a thick layer of blubber. Most species have a fin on the back which has no corresponding skeletal structure. The nostrils are located on the top of the head so that the animal may breathe while mostly submerged. Although they do resemble fish in body form, the cetaceans are of course true mammals; they produce live young which are nourished by milk from the mother's body.

38. Whale

"And God created great whales, and every living creature that moveth, which the waters brought forth abundantly, after their kind, and every winged fowl after his kind: and God saw that *it was* good" (Gen. 1:21).

"*Am* I a sea, or a whale, that thou settest a watch over me?" (Job 7:12).

"Son of man, take up a lamentation for Pharaoh king of Egypt, and say unto him, Thou art like a young lion of the nations, and thou *art* as a whale in the seas; and thou camest forth with thy rivers, and troubledst the waters with thy feet, and fouledst their rivers" (Ezek. 32:2).

"Now the Lord had prepared a great fish to swallow up Jonah. And Jonah was in the belly of the fish three days and three nights" (Jonah 1:17).

"For as Jonas was three days and three nights in the whale's belly; so shall the Son of man be three days and three nights in the heart of the earth" (Matt. 12:40).

Only 4 times is the whale named directly in the Bible. The Hebrew word *tanninim* for "whale" can also be rendered as "sea monster," or even as "dragon." Therefore it is not certain that "whale" is literally intended in such stories as that of Jonah and the whale.

Two or three species of whales existed in the Mediterranean with which the Israelites could have been familiar. Today, the skeletons of two species of baleen whales are kept in a museum at Beirut; one of the animals was brought ashore at Beirut and the other at Sidon, the place where Jonah was supposed to have landed.

The Greek word used in the Septuagint for the sea monster in the Book of Jonah was *ketos*. It was the same as *cetus* in the Latin, which meant any large sea animal. It was from these words that the whales and their related kind derived the name of their order—*Cetacea*.

One of the best stories found in the Old Testament is the story of Jonah and his travels. When one hears of Jonah a whale comes to mind, for this is presumably the "great fish" that swallowed that ancient prophet. However, among persons interested in the matter and those scientists and theologians who have bothered to look deeper, there is a wide divergence of opinion as to which animal did swallow Jonah (if any ever did). Though many agree with the old myth that it was a whale, many others have tried to prove that a large shark was the culprit.

A whale is not a fish, and the Bible specifically writes that it was a "great fish" that ingested Jonah. It may be presumed that the ancient sailors already knew the difference between a fish and a whale, for there are records even of a king of ancient Assyria going to sea to hunt whales off the Palestinian coast.

The story of Jonah is not a very unusual one for the ancient world, there being many similar myths about monsters swallowing men and the men coming out alive.

One large group of whales is definitely ruled out of the Jonah story, and these are the whalebone or baleen whales, of which the Blue Whale, the largest living animal, is a member. These animals have a very limited capacity when it comes to swallowing large objects. They feed by straining out the numerous small sea life in the water by means of a great number of parallel horny plates of whalebone, or baleen, suspended on the sides of the upper jaw. Their gullets are small, hardly capable of swallowing a large mouse, much less a grown man.

Toothed whales, of which the largest is the Sperm Whale (*Physeter catodon*), can reach a length of over 60 feet, with teeth about 7 inches long (in the lower jaw only). This is the whale normally thought of when the story of Jonah and the whale is related.

Sperm whales feed on much larger food than their relatives the baleen whales, swallowing giant squids in great numbers. Undigested fragments of squids of enormous size have been found in the stomachs of these whales by their captors.

Herman Melville in *Moby Dick* mentions the battles between the squid and the sperm. If food of this size can be swallowed, then the possibility of a man meeting the same fate is not altogether impossible. There is even an authenticated report of a whale being opened in whose stomach a 10-foot shark was found intact, so that a man would not have had too much trouble fitting into such a whale. However, whether he could survive the ordeal of being swallowed (alive) is another matter.

Actually, there is a *reported* case of a man being swallowed by a whale and living to tell about it. This was supposed to have happened in February, 1891, to a whaler by the name of James Bradley. He was eaten by a whale, and when on the next day the whale was captured he was taken out of it, still alive. He had lain unconscious in the stomach and his rescuers had difficulty in restoring him to his senses. It is alleged that it took a month of recuperation before he regained his sanity.

According to Roy Chapman Andrews, a former director of the Museum of Natural History and an authority on whales: "Many people asked me if the Bible story of Jonah and the whale is true. Could a man be swallowed by a whale? So I pushed my body partly down the throat of a dead sixty foot sperm whale. I could just squeeze through. A fat man couldn't have made it."

Sharks can also swallow men and other large animals, whole. A Great White Shark (*Carcharodon carcharias*) was captured on the California coast which had an entire sea lion weighing 100 pounds in its stomach, and in another case, a large Newfoundland dog was found in the stomach of another man-eater. These sharks are large, sleek fish of a predatory nature which might go after a man tossing about on the waves.

The Challenger Expedition, a scientific voyage, dredged some teeth from the Pacific Ocean which were 5 inches long, so that the shark would have been almost 100 feet long, easily capable of swallowing a man. Fossils of Eocene and Miocene sharks also indicate that these fish once reached enormous sizes.

Linnaeus, the Swede who is called the father of modern zoology, thought that the Great White Shark was the "great fish" mentioned in the Bible, though other types of sharks have also been credited with the feat. The Basking Shark is another candidate, and the one living species,

Cetorhinus maximus, can grow to a length of about 40 feet. It has a large mouth with minute teeth, and feeds through hoop-like gill arches 4 to 6 inches long. The Norwegian Bishop Gunner, in 1765, tried to prove this fish the culprit, but it has too small a gullet.

The largest shark is the Whale Shark (*Rhincodon typus*) which can weigh scores of tons spread over a 50-foot length. This fish has a huge mouth with tiny teeth, and though its size might indicate that a man could possibly be swallowed by it, once again it is a plankton feeder and has too small a throat.

One author, writing on this subject, said: "In certain theological commentaries we find the remarkable statement that, in 1758, a sailor fell overboard in the Mediterranean and was swallowed by a shark. The captain commanded to train a gun upon the man eater, and the monster was hit by a cannon ball. The shark vomited out the sailor who was picked up by a boat; he had hardly suffered any injury."

We now have seen several animals which might fit the specifications of the great fish that swallowed Jonah. If we look at the natural habits of these animals there is one that has the greatest likelihood of being the one referred to: the Great White Shark. First of all, most commentaries on the Bible and other sources seem to think that it was this fish, and not the whale, that did the swallowing.

Finally, there is quite a different theory by way of explanation of the myth. This stems from the fact that the Phoenicians carried on a regular and thriving whaling industry out of several ports along the Palestinian coast. There are references to this in classical literature. It has been pointed out that Jonah ostensibly left Israel for "the east" but appears to have gone *west.* The theory supposes that he actually left by ship for North Africa and later returned by a Phoenician whaling ship and the statement that he had been swallowed, then regurgitated, by a whale was an allegorical way of stating that he had been with the whalers and then was "disgorged by a whaling ship." Semitic storytellers delight in cloaking their meaning by saying something parallel, as it were. Hebrew poetry (typified by the Psalms) does not scan: instead, the couplets all say the same thing twice, but in different words. Finally, in support of this theory it has been pointed out that Jonah had very real political reasons for explaining his long absence, and particularly *where* he had spent this time.

Most whales would not make a meal of a man because they usually stick to a pretty rigid diet; the sperm, for example, feeds mostly on squid; others on small fish; and the baleen whales on tiny creatures that make up the plankton. The man-eating sharks, on the other hand, are found in this sea, and are not as choosy about their meals, and so might conceivably go for a person helpless in the water.

Chapter 8
Birds of the Bible

RATITES	39. Ostrich	Ranan	*Struthio camelus*
PELICANS	40. Pelican	Ka'ath	*Pelecanus onocrotalus*
WADERS			
Ardeidae	41. Heron	Anafash	*Ardea* spp.
	42. Bittern	Kippod	*Botaurus stellaris*
Ciconiidae	43. Stork	Chasidah	*Ciconia ciconia*
WATER-FOWL	44. Swan or Ibis	Tinshemeth	*Cygnus olor* or *Threskiornis aethiopica*
BIRDS OF PREY			
Accipitridae	45. Kite	Dayah	*Milvus milvus*
	46. Eagles	Nesher	*Aquila* spp. and *Circaetus gallicus*
Vulturidae	47. Vultures	Rawkam	*Gyps fulvus, Neophron percnopterus,* and *Aegypius monachus*
	48. Lammergeier	Peres	*Gypaetus barbatus*
Pandionidae	49. Osprey	Azniyyah	*Pandion halietus*
Falconidae	50. Falcon	Netz	*Falco* spp., *et al. gen.*
GAMEBIRDS	51. Peacock	Tucci	*Pavo cristatus*
	52. Partridges	Kore	*Ammoperdix heyi,* and *Alectoris graeca*
	53. Quail	Shelev	*Coturnix coturnix*
	54. Chickens	Tarnegol	*Gallus domesticus*
CRANES	55. Cranes	Agur	*Grus grus*
PLOVERS	56. Lapwing	Or-goor	*Vanellus vanellus*
PIGEONS	57. Doves	Yonah, Tor	*Columba livia* and *Streptopelia turtur*
CUCKOOS	58. Cuckoo	Shachaph	*Cuculus canorus*
OWLS	59. Eagle Owl	Yanshooph	*Bubo bubo*
	Little Owl	Cos	*Athene noctua*
	Scops Owl	Kippoz	*Otus scops*
	Tawny Owl	Lilith	*Strix aluco*
EXOTICS	60. Hoopoe	Dukipath	*Upupa epops*
SONGBIRDS			
Corvidae	61. Raven	Oreb	*Corvus corax*
Hirundinidae	62. Swallows	A-geor	*Hirundo rustica, et al.*
Fringillidae	63. Sparrows, etc.	Tsippor	(All small finches, weavers, etc.)

135

THE FLIGHTLESS BIRDS (*Ratitae*)

Under the title Ratites are grouped the flightless, ostrich-like birds. They are characterized by having lost the well-developed keel to the breastbone that serves as a place of muscle attachment in birds endowed with the power of flight. The wings are greatly reduced.

THE OSTRICH FAMILY (*Struthionidae*)

The ostriches are the largest of all living birds. The bulky body is covered with coarse plumage, but the long neck and head are practically naked. The beak has an extended gape which reaches back to the line of the eyes. The eyes are 2 inches in diameter, among the largest known among land vertebrates; this gives them a very wide field of vision. They are also endowed with a keen sense of smell.

A large male ostrich is nearly five feet high at the back and may weigh more than 300 pounds. The female is considerably smaller. The animal runs at speeds up to 40 miles per hour, and can cover 15 feet in a stride. In addition, the ostrich is capable of stretching itself to 7 feet. (It is not true that ostriches hide their heads in sand when confronted with dangerous situations.)

39. Ostrich

"*Gavest thou* the goodly wings unto the peacocks? or wings and feathers unto the ostrich? Which leaveth her eggs in the earth, and warmeth them in dust, And forgetteth that the foot may crush them, or that the wild beast may break them. She is hardened against her young ones, as though *they were* not her's: her labour is in vain without fear; Because God hath deprived her of wisdom, neither hath he imparted to her understanding. What time she lifteth up herself on high, she scorneth the horse and his rider" (Job 39:13–18).

The ostrich referred to in the Bible was probably a form of the African Ostrich, *Struthio camelus*. This species at one time flourished in parts of Asia, and until recent times inhabited Palestine, Syria, and Arabia. The ostrich is mentioned in the Bible more often than we might think. This is because three different Hebrew words have the primary meaning of "ostrich," although in many translations of the Bible they may be rendered "owl" or "peacock." The three words are *ya'anah*, which means greediness, *ranan*, which is the Hebrew word for ostrich (although some scholars have translated it peacock), and *notseh*, which means feathers.

The second of these words is used in the Book of Job in a long description of the large bird. This description is remarkably accurate, although it overrates the ostrich's renowned stupidity. It points out the beauty of the bird's black and white plumage, as well as its remarkable speed when running at full speed. In the charge of neglecting its young, however, the ostrich is maligned by the passage from Job. The ostrich egg is remarkably hardy and can withstand the high noonday temperatures in the desert. In the evening, when the weather cools, the ostrich returns to its eggs to keep them warm. Although it is true that ostriches will occasionally leave eggs "lying around," this is because the bird usually lays many more eggs than it can hatch. Some of the eggs which are laid outside of the nest, therefore, do not hatch, but serve as food for the birds that do hatch lest they go hungry in the barrenness of the desert. Another reference to the failing of the ostrich as a parent can be found in the Book of Lamentations, where the prophet Jeremiah says: ". . . the daughter of my people *is become* cruel, like the ostriches in the wilderness" (Lam. 4:3).

Because it makes its home in the desert, the ostrich is coupled several times with the dragon in the Bible as a dweller in desolate places. Isaiah says of Babylon that "owls [or ostriches] shall dwell there and satyrs shall dance there" (Isa. 13:21). In the same chapter the prophet foretells that Idumaea will become "an habitation of dragons [*var.* 'wild dogs'], *and* a court for owls" (Isa. 34:13). A similar reference is found in the Book of Jeremiah (50:39). The ostrich is mentioned in both Leviticus and Deuteronomy as an unclean bird. Its strange cry is compared to the sound of human lamentation in both the Book of Job (30:28–29) and the Book of Micah (1:8). The latter reads: "Therefore I will wail and howl, I will go stripped naked: I will make a wailing like the dragons, and mourning as the owls."

The low, dolorous sound referred to has been compared to "the hoarse lowing of an ox in pain," and is made by the ostrich at night. The daytime feeding sound, contrarily, is a hissing, chuckling noise.

The thighs of the ostrich are naked and powerful. The legs are long and robust, tipped with two short toes with claws resembling hoofs. The plumage of the male is black while the short feathers of the wings and tail are white. Females are grayish brown. In both sexes the neck is covered with down, and in some varieties the skin is red or blue in color. The call of the ostrich is quite penetrating and is suggestive of grief and woe; they also "roar" exactly like lions.

Ostriches cannot live in forests and prefer to remain in open spaces. They usually travel in flocks, in company with mammals such as zebras. In such a relationship each of the animals involved is helpful for the survival of the other. Ostriches are omnivorous. They feed extensively on fruit, seeds, and plants, but will also eat small mammals, reptiles, and insects. Though they enjoy bathing and drinking, they are able to go without water for days. They are among the most primitive of birds in respect to intelligence, with a brain no larger than a walnut.

Ostriches are polygamous. As the breeding season draws near, the males fight each other with their beaks and necks. They are surprisingly powerful animals. Each male usually mates with three or four females. The number of eggs "per harem" can be as high as 20, each egg weighing 3 pounds. The eggs possess strong, thick shells which protect the embryo from the heat of the desert. The female participates in incubation, but only by day and during cold spells. The male performs all of the nightly incubation. The female is endowed with camouflage coloration to protect it while incubating in daylight. Hatching time is 6 weeks, and soon the young are able to travel in coveys with the adults.

The life span of the ostrich is about the same as man's. The animals thrive in captivity. They are carefully protected in a number of African national parks. Otherwise, ostriches are found in desert regions. Unfortunately, the ostriches that used to inhabit the Bible lands have become extinct.

THE SWIMMERS (*Pelecaniformes*)

The Steganopodes are a large group of water birds that include the cormorants, darters, gannets, pelicans, and frigate birds. All are characterized by having very short legs, and by having the four whole toes connected by a web, which extends to their tips. The wings are either long and rounded or very elongated and pointed. All members of the Order are carnivores, living mostly on fish.

THE PELICAN FAMILY (*Pelecanidae*)

The pelicans are the largest members of the Order, and are chiefly characterized by the unique development of the beak. It is very long and flattened, with a large, expandable pouch affixed to the lower mandible. The whole structure acts as a large bag, with the upper mandible forming a lid. The body is massive, the neck long, and the head comparatively small. The wings are broad and large, and the tail broad and rounded. There are 8 species of pelican, 6 of which are found in the Old World. They prefer tropical or subtropical habitats, and live together in large communities.

The pelican's lack of proportion makes it difficult for it to rise from the water. To take off, it must first run awkwardly along the surface, pounding at the water with its legs. Despite their awkward appearance, pelicans are peerless aerial acrobats. This is made possible by the (normal to birds) possession of a skeleton of hollowed-out bones and by the presence of large air reservoirs in the body. The birds fly in groups, usually following a definite formation, with their wings beating in harmony. The flying formation is directed by the leader pelican.

Small fish are the diet of pelicans. Some pelicans hunt these by circling and diving, frequently disappearing underwater. The majority, however, land on the surface of the water and submerge only the fore-part of the body. White Pelicans (*Pelecanus onocrotalus*) often hunt in large groups, surrounding the fish in a circle. The circle is gradually narrowed and the fish are gobbled up. When underwater, the pelican moves its bill from side to side, the pouch remaining open. The length of the pouch may exceed 15 inches. It can hold up to 3 gallons, and on land it sometimes droops almost to the ground. The primary function of the sac is to assist the bird in catching food. It also helps the bird to keep cool in a very hot environment, because it provides a great deal of surface area for evaporation.

40. Pelican

"And these *are they which* ye shall have in abomination among the fowls; they shall not be eaten . . . And the swan, and the pelican, and the gier-eagle" (Lev. 11:13, 18).

"I am like a pelican of the wilderness; I am like an owl of the desert" (Ps. 102:6).

The pelicans of the Bible are *Pelecanus onocrotalus*, the typical white pelican of Eurasia and Africa. They are inhabitants of large inland lakes. They are capable of nesting in a variety of environments—on bare ground, on ledges, or in trees. The nest may be formed from pebbles or from sticks. Pelicans usually lay 2 to 4 eggs. The incubation time is about 6 weeks, and is performed by both sexes. The young remain another 5 weeks in the nest, and then wander about in company with other young. A number of pelicans feed their offspring partially digested fish, which the young birds obtain directly from their mothers' throats.

During the breeding season, these pelicans begin to sprout horns on the upper side of their bills. There is generally only one horn and it measures about 3 inches long and 3 inches tall. When the breeding season is over it falls off. Also during this season the coloration of the exposed areas of the legs and face of many species changes from gray to bright orange or red. At the same time the white feathers acquire a beautiful pink tint, originating from secretions of the oil gland and spread throughout the plumage by the bird as it preens.

The pelican, because it is a bird that feeds mostly on creatures of blood (fish), is listed in Leviticus and Deuteronomy as an unclean bird. There it goes under the Hebrew name *ka'ath*, which literally means "to vomit." It is believed that this name was given to the pelican because it stores great quantities of fish in its large mandibular pouch, and feeds its young by disgorging. There are several references to the *ka'ath*, in Isaiah (34:11) and in Zephaniah (2:14), where it is usually translated as "cormorant." It would probably be more accurate in these instances to use "pelican" instead.

One of the most interesting references to the pelican occurs in Psalm 102:6: "I am like a pelican of the wilderness," the Psalmist writes. Since the pelican is a water bird, and the wilderness mentioned in the Bible is usually taken to refer to the desert, some problem arises here. The solution of this apparent anomaly may be twofold. First, there is no reason not to accept wilderness as meaning any desolate place, such as the ocean, as well as the desert. Second, naturalists have on occasion observed that the pelican, when its pouch is full, will fly to some nearby desert area to digest its food. Often it will sit on its breast there for days in a most melancholy attitude, giving the Psalmist's image even further strength. On the other hand, these birds especially favor lakes in deserts such as Walker Lake and the Great Salt Lake in Nevada.

Because of the red tip at the end of its beak, and the strange manner in which it feeds its young, the pelican was thought by the ancients to feed its brood with its own blood. From this misbelief arose the medieval ecclesiastical emblem comparing the pelican to the feeding of the Church.

THE LONG-LEGGED WADERS (*Ciconiiformes*)

This Order contains five families. The best-known are those of the Herons, the Storks, and the Ibises. Apart from islands, they are world-wide in range on the land surfaces of the earth.

THE HERON FAMILY (*Ardeidae*)

The herons, egrets, and bitterns, which make up the Family *Ardeidae*, can generally be distinguished by their thin, compressed bodies and long, thin necks. The beak is straight, narrow, and pointed, with serrated cutting edges at the tip. Medium-length legs end, usually, in three-toed feet; the claw of the third toe being pectinated on the inner side. The heron family, the *Ardeidae*, contains more than 60 species and at least 15 genera. Its members are wading birds whose chief sources of food are fish, and other aquatic animals. All the members are remarkably alike in structure. They have long legs and a long, mobile neck which is S-shaped when drawn back. The bird uses its bill as a spear, triggered by a very powerful thrust.

The plumage of most of the species is soft. On the sides of the chest and rump there are usually small feathers that grow continuously and are crumbled by the bill into a powderlike substance which is used in preening the other feathers. In areas soiled by fish slime, this dust is rubbed in, to soak up the oil, and is finally combed out by the claws. The various groups of the *Ardeidae* are differentiated by the arrangement of these "powder downs."

During the breeding seasons, both males and females have specialized ornamental plumage on some part of the body. The plumage is also
a good means of protection for these birds. Herons are communal animals and practice group nesting; with, also, several different species
breeding in the same nesting area. Herons are known to migrate for
thousands of miles in order to breed. The heron nests in trees and low
bushes and lays from two to five eggs. It rests in groups near the water,
but may also trespass on suburban lawns and zoological gardens. The
nest is made from papyrus or sedge, by bending the living stems in a
circle and trampling them down with the feet. The birds arrive in
March and leave in September. They feed on fish, frogs, mice, snakes,
and beetles. The parents feed the young by regurgitation.

The most successful group of the heron subfamily contains the typical herons. More than half the species of the *Ardeidae* belong to this
group. This contains most of the typical (Biblical) herons, including the
Blue, Brown, Purple, and White Herons. These four species are contained within the Genus *Ardea*. The typical herons are medium to
large in size, with slim bodies and long bills. Most of these species are
gregarious.

41. Heron

"And the stork, the heron after her kind, and the lapwing, and the
bat" (Lev. 11:19).

The purple heron (*Ardea purpurea*) is one of 11 species of herons
found in Israel. It is a summer breeder and found in all parts of Palestine
where there is standing water, and it poses something of a threat to
fish conservation. Among the species of heron known to the Ancient
Hebrews were the Buff-backed Heron (*Buphus russatus*), also called
the White Ibis, the most common of the seven species found in the
Biblical area.

42. Bittern

"I will also make it a possession for the bittern, and pools of water;
and I will sweep it with the besom of destruction, saith the Lord of hosts"
(Isa. 14:23).

"But the cormorant and the bittern shall possess it; the owl also and
the raven shall dwell in it: and he shall stretch out upon it the line of
confusion, and the stones of emptiness" (Isa. 34:11).

"And flocks shall lie down in the midst of her, all the beasts of the
nations: both the cormorant and the bittern shall lodge in the upper
lintels of it: *their* voice shall sing in the windows; desolation *shall be*
in the thresholds: for he shall uncover the cedar work" (Zeph. 2:14).

Because of the shyness of the bittern, it is often used by the writers of the Bible to suggest places of desolation and loneliness.

Some Biblical scholars have said that the use of the word *kippod* in these references indicates not the bittern, but the hedgehog, or porcupine! They base this supposition on the similarity of the Hebrew to the Arab word *kunfod*, which means porcupine. Tristram has pointed out, however, that the bittern, which was particularly abundant in the swamps of the Tigris River, fits more ideally into these descriptions than the hedgehog.

Bitterns differ from herons in the possession of shorter legs and a shorter and more compact body. Most bitterns inhabit marshes, where it is easy for them to hide. Bitterns are remarkably proficient at camouflaging themselves. In situations of danger, they use their plumage to duplicate the color and shape of swamp vegetation. They actually seem to disappear before the observer's eyes. Herons, on the other hand, do not possess this ability and simply take flight when alarmed.

The large bitterns comprise 4 species which occur throughout the world. The members are brown in color and streaked in appearance. The best known of these species is the Old World bittern (*Botaurus stellaris*) and the American bittern (*B. lentiginosus*).

During the mating season the larynx of these birds is modified so as to produce their mysterious-sounding love songs. The body of the bittern twists in an unusual manner in harmony with these notes.

Like the herons, bitterns possess mobile cervical vertebrae which permit them to spear fish by the action of their head and long, pointed bill. They also produce a powder for the purpose of soaking up oil which has been acquired in contact with the fish. Unlike herons, bitterns nest alone in grassy marshes.

THE STORK FAMILY (*Ciconiidae*)

The storks are a group of large birds that can easily be distinguished from the heron family by the lack of pectination on the inner edge of the claw of the third toe, and also by the absence of the powder-down patches on the rump. The beak, which forms a long, compressed, sharply pointed cone, may be either turned up at the end or gaping in the middle. The body is plump, the legs are long, and the toes are connected by a short web. The wings are large, and the 12-feathered tail is short and rounded.

43. Stork

"And these *are they which* ye shall have in abomination among the fowls; they shall not be eaten, they *are* an abomination; the eagle, and the ossifrage, and the ospray . . . And the stork, the heron after her kind, and the lapwing, and the bat" (Lev. 11:13, 19).

"Where the birds make their nests: *as for* the stork, the fir trees *are* her house" (Ps. 104:17).

Storks are mutes, lacking a voice box. To compensate for this they clap their bills rapidly and loudly. There are 17 species of storks and storklike birds distributed throughout the tropical and temperate regions of the world. They fly in a soaring manner, with neck and legs stretched out. They feed primarily on small animals plucked from the waters of swamps. Their diet includes frogs, eels, lizards, rodents, birds, and insects. Some species prefer to eat carrion. Storks possess considerable communal instincts and hunt in flocks. Their nests are sturdy and may be built in trees, on ledges, or even on houses. Three to five eggs are laid, which are soon covered with stains. Incubation is performed by both parents and lasts a little longer than a month.

The White Stork (*Ciconia ciconia*) is the best-known member of the family. It is found in Europe and Asia and some parts of Africa. It reaches a length of 4 feet. It is a highly cherished bird and believed by some to be a harbinger of good fortune. The White Stork is not completely white. There is some black in its wings, the bill is red, and the legs are pinkish.

The storks which inhabit the more northern areas of Europe and Asia migrate in groups when the cold season approaches. Some, when they return home in the spring, actually return to the same nest they had left. Storks often have permanent mates. The male communicates with the female through a series of grotesque movements of his head, back, and neck.

The common stork of Palestine is this same *Ciconia ciconia*. In the early spring the birds are seen in large flocks, remaining for a while to hunt frogs, lizards, mice, and locusts. In the fall the flights are much less frequent, because of the prevailing west winds which drive the birds farther inland. Some birds remain through the summer. The sexes are very much alike in appearance. Also found in Palestine is the Black Stork (*Ciconia nigra*), which arrives in small flocks in spring and autumn. It is frequently seen in trees. Storks were forbidden as food by the Mosaic law.

The stork has always been one of mankind's favorite birds. Its loyalty to its young, its punctual nesting habits, and its steady migratory instincts have, even in popular terminology of our own day, associated it with human childbirth. It is still believed in many parts of the world that if a stork nests in a man's house good luck will surely follow. The Hebrew word for the stork—*chasidah*—translates literally as "kindness." Man's liking of the stork also has its practical aspect, for the stork feeds on snakes, other reptiles, and various forms of offal and garbage; thus, it actually purifies the area in which it comes to rest. It is no wonder that many Biblical figures made mention of the stork's fine habits, even going as far as to hold the bird up as an example for man. Jeremiah, for example, contrasts the regularity of the stork's migration with the more wayward habits of the people of his time: "Yea, the stork in the heaven knoweth her appointed times; and the turtle, and the crane, and the swallow, observe the time of their coming: but my people know not the judgment of the Lord" (Jer. 8:7).

The emphasis on the stork's being "in the heaven" alludes to the extraordinary phenomenon of stork migration in the Middle East. Voyaging by daylight (unlike most birds) the storks travel in vast flocks that spread out against the sky in a truly startling and beautiful manner. They rest for a while in the region, scattering over the land, and then continue their migration.

In the Book of Job the fine maternal instincts of the stork are held in contrast to the reputed negligence of the ostrich: "The wing of the ostrich beateth joyously; But are her pinions and feathers the kindly stork's?" (Job 39:13).

The nesting habits of the stork are described by the Psalmist: ". . . *as for* the stork, the fir trees *are* her house" (Ps. 104:17). This description has less meaning today, when storks often nest in man-made constructions, than it had in Biblical times, when the stork, seeking a nesting place close to its source of food, picked trees tall enough and strong enough to support the large platform of its nest. Of the trees in the Middle East none is more suited to the stork than the fir, and the Psalmist is recording an accurate and quite perceptive account of Nature.

The Biblical writers overestimated the strength of the stork's beautiful wings, as did many ancients in regard to many large birds. In Zechariah we read: "Then lifted I up mine eyes, and looked, and, behold, there came out two women, and the wind *was* in their wings; for they had wings like the wings of a stork; and they lifted up the ephah between the earth and the heaven" (Zech. 5:9). Actually, like most birds, the stork can lift and fly with only a very small weight because of its light construction. Still, the sight of the stork's 7-foot wingspan soaring across the sky remains as impressive for us as it obviously was for Zechariah.

THE WATERFOWL (Order, *Anseriformes*)

This group contains, as well as the swans, geese, and ducks, three large, semi-aquatic birds popularly called "Screamers" that inhabit South America. Apart from these rather aberrant birds, the waterfowl form a somewhat close-knit family.

THE DUCK FAMILY (*Anatidae*)

Although they vary greatly in size, the members of this group, which includes the ducks, swans, and geese, all have quite similar body forms. The legs are always short, and the first toe is generally smaller than the rest. With one exception the toes are completely webbed. The beak is relatively short, straight, and laterally expanded. The dense plumage is characterized by its ability to shed water. There are always 10 primary quills to the wings, although the number of tail feathers is variable. All members of the Order molt annually, and in the true ducks the males shed their contour feathers twice each year.

44. Swan

"And these *are they which* ye shall have in abomination among the fowls; they shall not be eaten, they *are* an abomination; the eagle, and the ossifrage, and the ospray . . . And the swan, and the pelican, and the gier-eagle" (Lev. 11:13, 18).

"*Of* all clean birds ye shall eat . . . But these *are they* of which ye shall not eat . . . The little owl, and the great owl, and the swan . . ." (Deut. 14:11, 12, 16).

The lists of unclean birds in Leviticus and Deuteronomy include the swan. The Hebrew word used is *tinshemeth*, a word that has been translated in some editions of the Bible as "ibis." The latter versions are probably more correct, since the swan is extremely rare in Egypt, while the sacred ibis is quite plentiful. Also, there is little reason to make the swan an unclean animal. Except for these dubious references there is no mention in the Bible of the swan, the goose, or the duck. This could be because of the dry climate of the Middle East; yet migrating waterfowl may swarm in the lakes of the region.

Waterfowl are the descendants of a very old Family, going back to Miocene times (about 35 million years ago). Today the Order is represented by about 140 species, scattered over every part of the world outside of Antarctica. Geese, swans, and ducks are superficially distinct, but quite similar in structure and behavior.

Waterfowl possess short legs—much shorter than their wings. The bill is short and straight. The plumage is thick and heavily underlaid with down. A number of waterfowl pluck their feathers to line their nests and conceal their eggs. There are 10 primary feathers and a variable number of tail feathers. Just after the breeding season, the primary feathers molt and the wing quills are shed at the same time. In this manner, the birds are often rendered incapable of flying for some time.

The eggs laid are uniform in coloration. The incubation period takes as long as 40 days in some species. Between 10 and 20 eggs are deposited.

The young are covered with down and can swim within a day after hatching.

Most waterfowl are gregarious, existing in flocks of great size. The species that nest in the northern areas of the world migrate during the fall and the spring in large numbers. After the breeding season, geese and swans move in family groups to the wintering grounds. The bond between male and female is incredibly strong, sometimes lasting the entire life of the couple. Since swans are known to be able to live to be nearly 100 years old, we can appreciate the intensity of the mating bond. In ducks, on the other hand, the bond lasts no more than a few years. In most species of waterfowl, incubation is the duty of the female, while the male assists in the feeding and protection of the young.

Many types of geese and swans fly by running in the water, pounding the surface with their webbed feet, and striking it with the tips of their wings. The speed of flight is as high as 45 to 50 miles per hour. A number of species fly in patterns guided by a leader.

Waterfowl are generally omnivorous in their eating habits, but a few species feed primarily on fish. Others prefer crustacea and shellfish, but most of them are pure vegetable feeders. The plumage of waterfowl is covered with oil secreted from a gland found near the base of the tail. This keeps the body covering waterproof and also is physiologically associated with the maintenance of the plumage and growth of the body.

In ancient times waterfowl abounded. Following the invasion by man of their habitats, the population of the group diminished woefully. In recent years there has been some effort to prevent these numbers from further diminishing.

THE BIRDS OF PREY (*Falconiformes*)

Generally known as the diurnal birds of prey, the Accipitrines include the vultures, lammergeiers, eagles, ospreys, hawks, falcons, and kites. All members of the Order are well adapted to their way of life, being equipped with a hooked beak and sharp, curved talons. The eyes are always located at the sides of the head, and the fourth toe is never reversible. Although the young resemble the owls in having a soft, downy coat, all develop a firm plumage in the adult. The whole group is carnivorous, but while some members kill their own prey, others live on carrion.

THE HAWK FAMILY (*Accipitridae*)

This, the first family of the Birds of Prey, contains the eagles, the short-winged hawks or buzzards, the kites, the harriers, and a number of tropical forms. The best known of these groups mentioned in the Bible is that of the eagles. The only other is that of kites. This is rather vague, and will be disposed of first.

45. Kite

The Black Kite (*Milvus nigrans*) is one of the most common scavenger birds of prey in Palestine, and is carefully protected by the people.
A strong analogy exists between the Hebrew and the Arabic words for
the bird. Besides the Black Kite, other species such as *M. regalis* are common in the Holy Land.

46. Eagles

Four species of eagle are found in Palestine: *Aquila chrysaëtos*,
A. naevia, *A. heliaca*, and *Circaëtus gallicus*. Eagles, as a whole, need no
description. Scripture often refers to the eagle in terms of its keen sight,
its swiftness, its longevity, and its care in training its young. The Jews
used the eagle as the symbol of the Assyrian, Babylonian, and Persian
kings. The Hebrew word *nesher* occurs with great frequency in the
Old Testament. While it is usually translated as eagle, Tristram argues
in favor of putting the griffon-vulture, a bird more like the eagle than the
vulture in its traits and habits, in its place. The argument need not be
resolved to point out the fascination of the ancients with large birds
of prey. The griffon-vulture has a head covered with white down, and
thus certainly better fits the reference in Micah: "Make thee bald, and
poll thee for thy delicate children; enlarge thy baldness as the eagle; for
they are gone into captivity from thee" (Mic. 1:16).

Eagles' heads are not bald. Likewise, the other references that follow
can apply to either bird.

The strength and swiftness of the eagle in flight are celebrated over
and over again in the Bible. The rising up of eagles is equated several
times with salvation. A notable example occurs in Isaiah: "But they that
wait upon the Lord shall renew *their* strength; they shall mount up with
wings as eagles; they shall run, and not be weary, *and* they shall walk,
and not faint" (Isa. 40:31).

In Job, the swiftness of the eagle is used in a vivid and moving
metaphor: "They are passed away as the swift ships; as the eagle *that*
hasteth to the prey" (Job 9:26). And when Moses warns the Children
of Israel of the dangers they face when the years in the desert end, he
summons forth an eagle image: "The Lord shall bring a nation against
thee from far, from the end of the earth, *as swift* as the eagle flieth; a
nation whose tongue thou shalt not understand . . ." (Deut. 28:49).
(Again, some versions of the Bible say that the bird is a vulture.)

The prophets make reference to the swift birds of prey over and over
again. Jeremiah tells his people their persecutors are "swifter than the
eagles of the heaven" (Lam. 4:19), and Ezekiel writes of: ". . . A great
eagle with great wings, longwinged, full of feathers, which had divers
colours, came unto Lebanon, and took the highest branch of the cedar

. . ." (Ezek. 17:3). In the Book of Proverbs (30:19), "The way of an eagle in the air" is said to be one of the three things that are beyond the writer's understanding. Yet, he still uses the eagle's flight to make a point: "Wilt thou set thine eyes upon that which is not? for *riches* certainly make themselves wings; they fly away, as an eagle toward heaven" (Prov. 23:5).

The Book of Job, so rich in natural lore, does not omit the eagle. The nesting habits and keen eyesight of the eagle (or vulture) are noted: "Doth the eagle mount up at thy command, and make her nest on high? She dwelleth and abideth on the rock, upon the crag of the rock, and the strong place. From thence she seeketh the prey, *and* her eyes behold afar off. Her young ones also suck up blood: and where the slain *are*, there *is* she" (Job 39:27–30). Jeremiah (49:16) also notes the bird "that dwellest in the clefts of the rock," and warns, "though thou shouldest make thy nest as high as the eagle, I will bring thee down from thence, saith the Lord."

Finally, the Bible twice makes a correspondence between the care of the eagle for its young, and the protection God offers the Children of Israel. In Deuteronomy we find: "As an eagle stirreth up her nest, fluttereth over her young, spreadeth abroad her wings, taketh them, beareth them on her wings: *So* the Lord alone did lead him, and *there was* no strange god with him" (Deut. 32:11–12). And in Exodus, God says to Moses: "Ye have seen what I did unto the Egyptians, and *how* I bare you on eagles' wings, and brought you unto myself" (Exod. 19:4).

THE VULTURE FAMILY (*Vulturidae*)

The Old World vultures are mainly characterized by their large size, and, with the exception of the lammergeiers, by a bare neck and head. Although there may be short, stubby down, true feathers are never found on the crown of the head. Usually the males are as large as, if not larger than, the females. The beak is long and compressed, and always extends straight for some distance, after which it is sharply curved. The third and fourth toes are joined by a membrane at their base; the third toe is always long and the first short. All the toes are equipped with long, slightly curved claws. Most members of the family feed chiefly on carrion. This group of birds is often regarded as a subfamily of the *Accipitridae*.

47. Vultures

The Bearded Vulture, or Lammergeier (*Gypaëtus barbatus*), is one of the largest and most magnificent birds of prey. It feeds on carrion, but will also hunt and kill animals on its own. It manages to eat bones by carrying them aloft and dropping them on rocks to break them apart.

The Griffon Vulture (*Gyps fulvus*) feeds mostly on carrion, but also on locusts and small tortoises. It is able to go without food for several days with no ill effects, but when it does break its fast it will gorge itself. Tristram describes a pet vulture of his that ate until it could no longer stand, and then rolled over helpless on its side and fell asleep. The strength of the bird's stomach is equal to its capacity. One is known to have eaten a half pound of arsenical soap with no other result than a violent fit of vomiting. Because of its bald head and neck, this vulture is quite possibly the eagle-headed bird depicted on Assyrian sculpture, and referred to in Mic. 1:16.

The confusion that exists among Biblical references to scavenger birds, such as the debate over the proper translation of the word *nesher* (eagle or griffon vulture?), extends here. The Hebrew word *dayah* is usually rendered as vulture, while the word *ayah* is taken to mean kite. Tristram, however, argues that *dayah* is actually a kite, and points out that in a least one place (Job 28:7) it is translated as vulture. In Leviticus and Deuteronomy, the word used in the list of unclean birds (Lev. 11:14 and Deut. 14:13) is *ayah*, and it is followed by the expression, "after its kind," which may indicate that both types of scavenger are taken together generically and may be treated as such. (This also explains the similarity, suggesting a single root, of the two Hebrew words.)

Above the battlefields and carnage of the Old Testament sits the vulture, the most detested of Nature's scavengers. It is not always named, but again and again the phrase, "fowls of the air," is written to describe eaters of dead flesh. In the Book of Kings, for example, it is written: "Him that dieth of Jeroboam in the city shall the dogs eat; and him that dieth in the field shall the fowls of the air eat: for the Lord hath spoken *it*" (I Kings 14:11). And again, in Psalms: "O God, the heathen are come into thine inheritance; thy holy temple have they defiled; they have laid Jerusalem on heaps. The dead bodies of thy servants have they given *to be* meat unto the fowls of the heaven, the flesh of thy saints unto the beasts of the earth" (Ps. 79:1–2).

In several places the Bible becomes more specific, but usually uses the vulture in an emblematic or symbolic sense. It represents death, and as such is used by the prophets as a symbol of the desolation that will overtake the wicked cities. Hosea warns the Hebrews in these words: "*Set* the trumpet to thy mouth: *he shall come* as an eagle against the house of the Lord, because they have transgressed my covenant, and trespassed against my law" (Hos. 8:1).

Both Isaiah and Zephaniah use the vulture similarly. The former, in describing the destruction to befall Edom, says: "There shall the great owl make her nest, and lay, and hatch, and gather under her shadow; there shall the vultures also be gathered, every one with her mate" (Isa. 34:15). And the latter foresees the downfall of Nineveh in these terms: "And flocks shall lie down in the midst of her, all the beasts of the nations: both the cormorant and the bittern shall lodge in the upper lintels of it: *their* voice shall sing in the windows; desolation *shall be* in the thresholds: for he shall uncover the cedar work" (Zeph. 2:14).

Two other vultures are common in Palestine and were doubtless known to the Hebrews. These are the Black Vulture (*Aegypius monachus*) and Pharaoh's Vulture (*Neophron percnopterus*).

48. Lammergeier

"But these *are they* of which ye shall not eat: the eagle, and the ossifrage, and the ospray" (Deut. 14:12).

Peres is the Hebrew word for ossifrage, believed to be the Lammergeier, the largest of the vultures. This word, however, is an old English name for the Osprey of the British Isles. The Lammergeier is also called the "Bearded Vulture," because of the long, stiff hairs emerging from the face area. After the jackals and smaller vultures reduce the carcasses to the bone, this huge bird crushes the bones to obtain the marrow, or swallows the pieces intact.

THE OSPREY FAMILY (*Pandionidae*)

The Osprey or Fish-Hawk seems to occupy a position midway between the vultures and the other birds of prey. They differ from the latter in having the fourth toe reversible, a feature they share with the quite unrelated owls. The tendons of their powerful legs have been found to be more like those of the vultures than the falcons, which latter they resemble in all other respects.

There is only one species of Osprey (*Pandion haliaëtus*) distributed all over the temperate and tropical regions of the world.

49. Osprey

The Osprey is mentioned in the Bible only in the lists of clean and unclean birds in Deuteronomy and Leviticus. Its place on the list of the unclean birds, alongside the eagle, the vulture, the pelican, the stork, and others, undoubtedly is due to its carnivorous feeding habits. It is as large as some eagles and possesses a very sharp bill. The bird frequents coastal waters of continents but is also seen along the edges of inland rivers and lakes. It is also found in the islands of Oceania, where few hawks dwell.

The Osprey feeds primarily on fish. Some at times eat other marine life, such as the poisonous sea snakes of the Pacific and Indian Oceans.

When hunting for fish, it flies from 50 to 150 feet over the sea. When it spots the fish it furls its wings and darts down into the water. It pierces the fish with its needle-sharp talons and then rises rapidly from the water, and flies off to a tree or cliff to devour its catch.

The Osprey flies very smoothly, soaring gracefully. Unlike other hunting hawks, it has the outer toe reversible, and the claws are approximately the same in length with a strong curvature. The pads on the underside of the toes are modified with scales to aid the bird in grasping slippery victims.

In America the Osprey usually nests in trees; in Europe it prefers to nest on the edges of a cliff. There may be as many as 30 nests close together. Both sexes participate in the construction of the nest. The same nest may be occupied year after year until it reaches a depth and width of 6 feet. Two or three eggs are laid, which are white with blotchings of purple, orange, red, lilac, and black. The female does most of the incubation, a task which requires 5 weeks. For several weeks following hatching, she performs most of the brooding and feeding. Consequently, the male's chief duty is to hunt and carry food to its mate and the young. The nestlings do not leave the nest for almost 2 months.

Ospreys have a reputation for defending their eggs and young with violence, making it difficult for intruders to rob the nests. The male and the female are alike in appearance; the lower parts, neck, and head are white and the back and wings chiefly dark brown. The chest has a collar of brown spots and the head sports a blackish crest. The female is 2 feet in length, about 4 inches larger than the male.

THE FALCON FAMILY (*Falconidae*)

Comprising the hunting hawks or falcons, the falconets, and the aberrant caracaras of the New World, the *Falconidae* have a number of peculiar characteristics. The feathers have well-developed aftershafts, and the nostrils are separated by a median partition. The head is always covered with true feathers. In many species the females exceed the males in size. Although most of the *Falconidae* exist mainly on the prey they kill themselves, some eat carrion, and a few feed on honeycomb.

The word "hawk" is, in the English language—and more so in the various present-day regional forms of that language—a most ambiguous word. Normally, but by no means exclusively, it is reserved to designate the smaller members of the *Accipitridae* but it is interchangeable with Falcon in many cases; while such names for falcons as Duck-Hawk, Pigeon-Hawk, and so forth are in common usage. While there are short-tailed or true hawks among the 20 or so Accipiters in the region, it seems more likely that falcons are referred to in the Bible. However, the writers of the Bible used the names *raah, ayah, dayah,* and *daah,* rather indiscriminately; or, alternatively and more likely the translators did so; while the Hebrew word *netz* seems to cover all of them.

This Hebrew word appears in the Old Testament 3 times, and certainly covers several of the small predatory hawks that inhabit the Biblical lands, including the Kestrel (*Tinnunculus alaudarius*), the Lesser Kestrel (*Tinnunculus cenchris*), the Hobby Hawk (*Falco eleonoroe*), and the Black-shouldered Hawk (*Elanus coeruleus*). Two of the 3 mentions of the word appear in the lists of unclean birds in Deuteronomy and Leviticus. Twice the word is followed by the phrase "after its kind," indicating that the writer was well aware that several different species of bird were included in the term. The third appearance of the hawk is in the Book of Job which reads: "Doth the hawk fly by thy wisdom . . . ?" (Job 39:26).

Another mention is in Leviticus: "And these *are they which* ye shall have in abomination among the fowls; they shall not be eaten, they *are* an abomination; the eagle, and the ossifrage, and the ospray . . . And the owl, and the night hawk, and the cuckow, and the hawk after his kind . . ." (Lev. 11:13, 16).

Falcons are predatory birds, feeding upon the flesh of a variety of animals. They come in a remarkable variety of sizes, but they are very similar in structure and habits. They have strong feet with three toes pointing forward and one backward, all bearing long, sharp claws. The bill is sturdy and hooked and the eyes, although laterally located, look straight forward. The eyes are considerably developed. The structure of the eye is so arranged that the hawk is capable of using monocular vision for nearby objects and binocular vision for distant objects. No wonder the expression, "eyes like a hawk's," is so widely used in everyday speech.

The hawk is a powerful flyer. Some types can swoop to the ground or water from a perch in a tree; others are capable of diving from above and killing their prey in the air while in full flight. The claws grasp the prey; the feet hold the victim down and the bill dismembers it.

50. *Falcons (Long-tailed Hawks)*

In most species, the female is considerably bigger than the male. The usual mating relationship is one male per one female. In many species the initial couple remains together for life. Both members take part in building the nest, incubating the eggs, and protecting and feeding the young. Most hawks build their nests in trees, the structure usually consisting of a platform of sticks. Many species build them on cliffs, and some even build them on the ground. The number of eggs varies from 1 to 7. The incubation period is 1 or 2 months. The young are born sightless and often cannot stand until they are 3 weeks old. They remain in the nest a few months. In many species they are nearly as large as the adults at the time of their departure from the nest, although the plumage is markedly different.

The best-known members of the family belong to the genus *Falco*, which includes the famous Peregrine. These birds are swift, formidable killers. They have been used for hunting since ancient times. The Hebrew did not hunt with hawks, mainly because these animals were considered unclean.

The *Falconidae* are, as has been said, divided into a number of subfamilies. The most primitive of these includes the Laughing Falcons of Central and South America. These birds have a white head and black mask. The Caracaras form an aberrant subfamily, found in the forests of Florida and of Central and South America. They feed largely on carrion. To the third subfamily belong the falconets, which include some of the smallest of the birds of prey. Some of these creatures are no more than 6 inches long. The true falcons, of which there are 37 species found over all the continents and large islands apart from Antarctica, are the most aggressive of all birds. All of them have sharply pointed wings, a short neck, and legs covered with what look like "pants." Some are found in coastal areas, while others prefer dry inland areas.

It is hard to determine what particular species of falcon is being referred to in the Bible. One possibility is the Peregrine. This land bird has one of the widest ranges of any bird in existence. It is found as far north as the Arctic, and as far south as the southern tips of Africa, India, and South America. There are very few varieties within the species, despite its remarkable range. The familiar Duck-Hawk is none other than the American representative of this species.

The sexes of the Peregrine are very much alike. The upper parts are dark grayish in color, with the head and flight feathers much darker. The breast of the bird is white with dark spotting. Around the lower abdomen, legs, and undersurface of the wing, it resembles a zebra. Another possibility for the Biblical falcon is the European Kestrel, which is found throughout Europe and Asia. It has a habit of nesting chiefly in old crow nests. It hovers as it searches for prey, and feeds primarily on insects and small birds. It has a reputation for adjusting well to city life. Its incubation period is about a month and the young remain in the nest for 4 or 5 weeks.

Falcons hunt in a variety of specialized ways. Some feed exclusively on insects which they capture in the air. Others prefer to hover over and pounce on lizards, frogs, beetles, and grasshoppers. Many eat rabbits and small rodents and birds.

The boldest of the falcons live on flying game. Several species of these birds have been trained by man to hunt a variety of game birds, even birds of greater size than themselves. Some have even been trained to attack other birds of prey. Such fights were once witnessed with enjoyment by spectators, somewhat in the same manner as cockfighting. One of the most important assets of hunting falcons is their ability to reach speeds up to 120 miles per hour.

THE GAME BIRDS (*Galliformes*)

Such game birds and fowl as the peacocks, grouse, pheasants, quails, partridges, turkeys, and chickens are all included in the Order *Gallinae*. All have a compact body, with a rather long neck, and a large, rounded head. The legs vary in length, but are always strong and well adapted for running on land. The four toes are usually equipped with slightly curved, powerful claws. The wings are carried close to the body, and the tail exhibits a great variety in both shape and form. The young, which are able to run soon after being hatched, are covered with either soft down or feathers.

THE PHEASANT FAMILY (*Phasianidae*)

This Family, including the peacocks, pheasants, grouse, partridges, quail, and the true fowl (chickens) comprises the bulk of the typical game birds. All have scaled legs and feet, which are often armed with one or more pairs of sharp spurs.

51. Peacock

The peacock is not a natural inhabitant of the Biblical lands, thus was not known to the Hebrews until the time of Solomon, whose far-flung navy reached India's shores and brought home for the wise king's pleasure several of these beautiful birds. Thus, we find the peacock mentioned only once in the Old Testament. The first book of Kings describes the treasures collected by Solomon's sailors, and lists the peacock among them. "For the king had at sea a navy of Tarshish . . . bringing gold, and silver, ivory, and apes, and peacocks" (I Kings 10:22).

Curiously, the peacock is never used by the prophets to point up a maxim, for in our own day the bird has become a symbol for vanity and pride.

The Hebrew word used in describing Solomon's peacocks is *tucciyim*, which most commentators believe is not a Hebrew word at all but a corruption of the Indian word which designated the bird. In Ceylon, the peacock is still called *tokei*, a similarity too strong to be coincidental.

Some versions of the Book of Job have a line translated: "The wings of the peacock beateth joyfully" (Job 39:13). The Hebrew word used in that instance is *ranan*, which most modern scholars now agree should be translated properly as "ostrich."

After the time of Solomon, the peacock spread throughout the Mediterranean area. It was well known by the Greeks and the Romans, and Alexander the Great so prized the beauty of these birds that he forbade his soldiers to kill any of them. All of this increases the mystery of why the peacock is not mentioned in the later Biblical books.

52. Partridge

The Hebrew word *kore* (meaning "caller") refers to the partridge (and the francolin), and is found twice in the Scriptures. David, remonstrating with Saul for his persecution of the future king, says: "Now therefore, let not my blood fall to the earth before the face of the Lord: for the king of Israel is come out to seek a flea, as when one doth hunt a partridge in the mountains" (I Sam. 26:20). The passage refers to the fact that the partridge was used as food by the Hebrews. In several places the method of hunting birds such as the partridge is told. Jeremiah says of wicked men: ". . . they lay wait, as he that setteth snares: they set a trap, they catch men. As a cage is full of birds, so *are* their houses full of deceit: therefore they are become great, and waxen rich" (Jer. 5:26–27).

And in the Apocryphal book of Ecclesiasticus there is a reference to a "decoy partridge in a cage" (11:30). This probably refers to the method of setting a captured partridge with its eyes sewn shut amidst a snaggle of bird traps, so that its cries would attract its fellows. David's reference may be to another method of hunting partridges: by throwing stones and sticks at the fleeing bird which, when frightened, runs along the ground rather than flying to escape its pursuer.

Another mention of the partridge, in Jeremiah, wrongly accuses the bird of stealing eggs. Speaking of those who win riches "not by right," the prophet uses a bird metaphor: "*As* the partridge sitteth *on eggs,* and hatcheth *them* not; *so* he that getteth riches, and not by right, shall leave them in the midst of his days, and at his end shall be a fool" (Jer. 17:11).

Tristram argues that the prophet's image refers not to the fact that the bird steals the eggs of others, but rather that it lays many, many eggs which were (and still are) stolen by men and other animals for food, and thus she sits upon a brood that is "not brought forth."

The most familiar partridge, and a likely candidate for the Biblical reference, is the Hungarian or Red-legged partridge. It is medium-sized, with grayish plumage and a black, horseshoe-shaped patch on its abdomen. The bird is a very capable flyer, especially noted for its rapid take-off. It inhabits the middle portions of Europe and Asia between sea level and 15,000 feet. It was introduced to America a long time ago and to this date nearly a quarter of a million of the birds have entered the country.

Another candidate for the Biblical partridge is the *Ammoperdix heyi* (Hey's Sand Partridge). This is a desert partridge found in North Africa and Palestine. In Palestine, it is seen in the Jordan Valley and the Dead Sea Depression. It is also found in the regions of Sinai. It is very adept at running and jumping, and can ascend nearly perpendicular cliffs.

The bird is medium in size and sandy colored. Underneath, it is brown and white. The female is grayish in color. It deposits a clutch of 8 to 14 eggs during the month of April, placing them in a depression in the ground.

Closely related to the partridges are the Francolins (Genus, *Fracolinus*) to which belong 35 species extending over Eurasia and Africa. The majority of these birds have sharply spurred legs, some of them possessing twin sets of spikes. The francolins are found in most bushy grasslands. In the Near and Middle East they are known as "black partridges."

53. Quail

Quail also belong to the family *Phasianidae*, in company with the peacocks, pheasants, etc. There are 57 genera and 170 species of quail which vary considerably in size. The majority of these animals have bodies shaped like tiny chickens with naked legs and toes. In most cases the males are more highly colored. The family is divided into a New World subfamily and an Old World subfamily. The New World quails, the *Odontophorinae*, consist of 34 species that are found in most areas of the New World and are believed to be the descendants of an ancient influx from the Old World.

Most of the species are not migratory, the significant exception being the European Quail (*Coturnix coturnix*). This is the quail to which the Bible refers. It has a considerable range in Eurasia and Africa. It is a little smaller than the average American quail, possessing a white throat and brown and black markings on the body. The belly is white. It feeds mainly on weed seeds and insects and for this reason is very helpful to man. It breeds on the ground, depositing 9 to 15 eggs spotted with dark brown. It is possible to capture immense numbers of quail during the fall migration in the Mediterranean regions, by the use of nets. This bird is little bigger than a starling.

The quail is a popular game and table bird in Europe, Asia, and Africa. The animal is characterized by a unique method of defense. A number of the animals gather together in circles on the ground. The members of the circle are usually from the same family. They sit with their tails in and their heads out. When the attacker approaches, the birds leap into flight in all directions, thus confusing the invader. This technique is not only used for defensive purposes but also is a successful means of procuring warmth. Forms which are related to the European quail include the Australian Stubble-Quail (*C. pectoralis*), the African quail (*C. delegorguei*), and the Indian Rain-Quail (*C. coromandelica*). "*The people* asked, and he brought quails, and satisfied them with the bread of heaven" (Ps. 105:40).

Although quails occur in only one important Biblical incident, their importance is great. When the Hebrews left Egypt and entered the desert, fears arose among the people that they had been led there to starve. The Hebrews complained to Moses, and, as the Bible tells us, were heard by God who miraculously sent down a rain of manna from the heavens. The narrative continues: "And the Lord spake unto Moses, saying, I have heard the murmurings of the children of Israel: speak unto them, saying, At even ye shall eat flesh, and in the morning ye shall be filled with bread; and ye shall know that I *am* the Lord your God. And it came to pass, that at even the quails came up, and covered the camp; and in the morning the dew lay round about the host" (Exod. 16:11–13). Years later, while still in the desert, the Hebrews again tell Moses of their hunger: "And there went forth a wind from the Lord, and brought quails from the sea, and let *them* fall by the camp, as it were a day's journey on this side, and as it were a day's journey on the other side, round about the camp, and as it were two cubits *high* upon the face of the earth. And the people stood up all that day, and all *that* night, and all the next day, and they gathered the quails: he that gathered least gathered ten homers: and they spread *them* all abroad for themselves round about the camp" (Num. 11:31–32).

The Biblical scholar William Gladstone has estimated from these passages that 9 million quail were gathered by the hungry Israelites. While this figure is probably a distortion, there is nothing impossible about the story. Quails migrate in great flocks, flying with the wind at low heights because of their weak wings. (That explains the reference to two cubits, approximately 40 inches.) Furthermore, quails are excellent food sources. The position taken by some scholars that the bird was actually a stork, whose meat is tough and difficult to eat, seems quite untenable.

The Psalmist remembers the Lord's bounty to the wandering Hebrews. Psalm 78 reads: "He rained flesh also upon them as dust, and feathered fowls like as the sand of the sea . . ." (Ps. 78:27), while Psalm 105 recalls how "*The people* asked, and he brought quails, and satisfied them with the bread of heaven" (Ps. 105:40).

54. Chickens (Domestic Fowl)

There is no mention in the Old Testament of what are today the most well-known species of birds—that is, the barnyard fowl or chicken. This is primarily because the Israelites did not domesticate birds. At times they did semi-domesticate doves and pigeons (*see* DOVES, page 161), keeping them in cages, but they did not purposefully raise birds as sources of food. This is not denied by the mention of eggs in the Book of Job (". . . or is there *any* taste in the white of an egg?", (Job 6:6), for the eggs of several wild birds were readily available to the nomadic Hebrews. In fact, the dietary laws in Deuteronomy (22:6–7) tell specifically when the eggs of a wild bird may be taken from the nest.

In the New Testament, which was written at a later date, hens, cocks, and chickens are all mentioned, indicating that the art of domesticating this species had been introduced. A well-known New Testament story —the prophecy of Jesus that Peter would deny him three times before the morning crow of a rooster—is told in the Book of Matthew.

All our present-day domestic fowl appear to have been developed from one or two species of Jungle Fowl indigenous to the Oriental Region, whence they were carried west to Europe and on to North America; north to China and Japan; and possibly east, across the Pacific to South America. The domestic fowl had definitely reached Egypt by 1350 B.C., for a very clear painting of a cock was found on a potsherd in the tomb of Tutankhamen in A.D. 1923 and was figured by Carter, the tomb's discoverer. Thus, the Hebrews probably knew the chicken from before the Exodus. However, apparently they did not adopt it until it was reintroduced to them by the Romans.

THE CRANES (*Gruiformes*)

Most of the features that distinguish the cranes, bustards, and several other families of birds as a group, from the other bird orders, are trivial in character. All have a schizognathous, or slit, palate, and have active, down-covered young. The angle of the lower jaw is truncated; either the number of toes is reduced to three, or, if four toes are present, the breastbone is not notched. (Rewrite from E. T. Gilliard's *Living Birds of the World.*)

THE CRANE FAMILY (*Gruidae*)

The cranes are large wading birds that have a marked outward similarity to the herons and storks. They are characterized by elongated legs and neck, and by a long beak. The wings are long and composed of 10 primary quills. The 12-feathered tail is short. The small first toe is elevated above the other three; and all undergo a semiannual molt.

55. *Crane*

The crane is identified twice in the Bible under its Hebrew name *agur*. The references encompass perhaps the two most distinctive features of the bird, its very conspicuous migratory habits, and its sound. Jeremiah, as we have already seen, used the migration of birds as a contrast to the wayward habits of the Israelis (*see* STORK, page 142). "Yea, the stork in the heaven knoweth her appointed times; and the turtle, and the crane, and the swallow, observe the time of their coming: but my people know not the judgment of the Lord" (Jer. 8:7). The feelings of a man oppressed are recalled in Isaiah, and the description includes the line: "Like a crane, *or* a swallow, so did I chatter; I did mourn as a dove: mine eyes fail *with looking* upward: O Lord, I am oppressed; undertake for me" (Isa. 38:14). The description also adds the words, "moan of a dove," so that the combination of the three distinctive sounds of these birds seems to be equated with the sound of a man in sorrow.

The cranes are tall, stately birds found throughout the tropical and temperate regions of the world, except for areas in Oceania and South America. There are 14 known species, some of which are on the brink of extinction. Cranes are named after their plumage, coloration, geographical extent, or, as in the case of the Whooping Crane (*Grus americana*) of North America, for their call. Most cranes are about 5 feet tall and have large wingspreads. The legs and neck are long. The long, powerful bill serves as a sharp hammer for killing snakes, small alligators, and frogs.

All cranes have remarkably powerful voices, and their calls are believed to carry for miles. They have a specialized windpipe with large convolutions which lengthen as the crane ages. The trachea of the Whooping Crane is 5 feet in length. This vocal power comes in handy during migration where it is used to keep the birds together. There is usually a flock leader that does the calling. The migratory flights of cranes can be very long in duration. The flock is often large in number, consisting of up to 2000 members. It exhibits certain pattern formations in accordance with the direction and intensity of the wind and with the arrangement of the bird's anatomy. The legs are carried straight back, with head and neck fully extended forward. Whooping Cranes fly at heights of up to 13,000 feet.

After spending the winter in the south, many species return northward to breed. When the flock arrives, it splits into pairs which engage in very attractive dances. The male bends his neck and head forward and leaps high above the female while he whoops. The female responds by also jumping high into the air. After mating, cranes live in pairs. There are only 2 eggs laid and the breeding is once a year. The eggs are placed in a nest of grasses and reeds constructed by both partners on marshy ground. The nest is not hidden, but is watched carefully by the parents. Both sexes partake in incubation, which lasts about a month. The young are capable of leaving the nest on the day of their hatching, despite the fact that they are only $\frac{1}{100}$ the size of the parents. However, they are usually fed and protected by their parents for long periods. They are not able to fly until they are 4 months old, and usually do not acquire their full adult plumage for 2 years.

Cranes are most abundant in Eurasia, partly because many people there believe that harming cranes brings bad luck. The most common species is *Grus grus*, or the European Crane. This is the species referred to in the Bible. Cranes are useful to the natives because of their ability to kill snakes, insects, and small rodents. In India, their young are captured and used as watchdogs. The most beautiful cranes in the world are found in Africa.

THE PLOVERS (*Charadriiformes*)

This is a very large assemblage of only vaguely related birds that includes many shorebirds, snipe, oystercatchers, avocets, pratincoles, gulls, skuas, terns, skimmers, auks, guillemots, and puffins. Most of these are basically marine or littoral inhabitants and so did not come to the attention of the Hebrews who were an inland people. Nevertheless, some are purely land-living forms, and one of these impressed the Israelites.

THE TYPICAL PLOVERS (*Charadriidae*)

These in turn are divided into 3 groups: the True Typical Plovers— a fine example of the inefficiency of the popular, as opposed to the Linnaean system of Latinized binomial nomenclature—of which there are some 35 species known from all over the world; the Turnstones and Surfbirds, 3 aberrant forms; and the Vanellines or Lapwings, of which there are a dozen species. The last form quite an assemblage with a rather wide variety of form and habit.

56. Lapwing

Just which lapwing is meant by the Hebrew name *or-goor* is uncertain but most scholars now agree that it is the Common Lapwing (*Vanellus vanellus*, or *cristatus*) of Eurasia. This is a most elegant bird, iridescent dark green with flashes of copper above and white below with a black chest band. It is about a foot long, has long legs and stubby wings. From the back of the head a curved crest ascends. It lays 4 eggs—the "plovers' eggs" that were once a great table delicacy. It also migrates from Europe and central Asia to Africa and is common at all times in

Palestine. It is, for the most part, an inland dweller, and has a most distinctive cry.

THE PIGEON TRIBE *(Columbiformes)*

The doves, pigeons, and sandgrouse form a well-defined, easily recognizable group. All have a rather compact body and a moderately large head, set on a graceful neck. The beak is swollen at the extremity, and has soft skin containing the nostrils covering its basal portion. Usually, there is a marked distinction between feathered and unfeathered areas on the body.

57. *Dove (Rock-dove, Turtle-dove)*

The dove is indisputably the most important bird in the Bible. It first gains prominence in the story of Noah. After Noah, his family, and the multitude of animals had been cooped up in the ark for 40 days and nights, the old man sent forth a raven which did not return. He then sent forth a dove, which, unable to find dry land, returned to the ark. Seven days later he sent forth the dove once more, and when the bird returned it had an olive branch clasped in its beak. God had made his peace with earth, and to this very day the dove holding an olive branch is a symbol of that peace. Seven more days passed, and once again Noah released the dove. When it did not return, Noah knew that the waters had receded, and he removed the top of the ark, releasing the animals and the birds to go out into the world and repopulate it.

The importance of the dove in the beginnings of Judaism should not be underestimated. Only it and the pigeon were thought pure enough for sacrifice to God. In fact, when Abram, the founder of the Children of Israel, performed a sacrifice to the Lord, he offered up a "she goat of three years old, and a ram of three years old, and a turtledove, and a young pigeon" (Gen. 15:9). The Book of Leviticus mentions the dove several times, telling on what occasions it should be offered up to God. If a man could not afford to sacrifice a sheep, the Law of Leviticus tells him to offer up either two turtledoves or two pigeons (Lev. 5:7). Similarly, the turtledove is mentioned as a sacrifice for purification of lepers (Lev. 14:22), and a Nazarite is enjoined to sacrifice a pair of doves to purify himself (Num. 6:10). Also, probably because the dove is a symbol of maternal devotion and purity, the Law says that the mother of a newborn infant shall offer two doves to God (Lev. 12:8).

The prophets did not ignore the gentleness of the dove. Isaiah seems to indicate that the doves lived with the Israelites in a semidomesticated way when he says: "Who *are* these *that* fly as a cloud, and as the doves to their windows?" (Isa. 60:8). And on two occasions, when describing the wailing of man's soul, he refers to the mournful cooing of the dove:

"We roar all like bears, and mourn sore like doves: we look for judgment, but *there is* none; for salvation, *but* it is far off from us" (Isa. 59:11). Ezekiel refers both to the cooing of the dove and its habitat in the rocky hills when he writes: "But they that escape of them shall escape, and shall be on the mountains like doves of the valleys, all of them mourning, every one for his iniquity" (Ezek. 7:16). Jeremiah makes a similar reference to the dove "*that* maketh her nest in the sides of the hole's mouth" (Jer. 48:28).

The Psalms make reference to several of the dove's features. The beauty of the dove's feathers as they shimmer in the bright sunlight is described: "Though ye have lien among the pots, *yet shall ye be as* the wings of a dove covered with silver, and her feathers with yellow gold" (Ps. 68:13). The graceful flight of the bird is also invoked: "And I said, Oh that I had wings like a dove! *for then* would I fly away and be at rest" (Ps. 55:6). And it is the humbleness, the meekness, and the gentleness of the dove that leads the Psalmist to ask the Lord not to lead the "soul of thy turtledove unto the multitude *of the wicked* . . ." (Ps. 74:19). These same characteristics make the bird prominent in the New Testament, where it is on several occasions transformed into a symbol for Jesus.

Doves are monogamous and pay a great deal of attention to their mates. The nest is usually small and delicate. Most of the species lay only 2 eggs which are shining white in color. Both sexes help to construct the nest and both participate in incubation, the female by night and the male by day. Incubation lasts 2 to 3 weeks. The young are hatched with their eyes sealed and stay in the nest for 12 to 18 days. During the first 2 weeks the young are nourished with "pigeon's milk" a substance regurgitated by both parents. The milk is secreted by the wall of the stomach.

Doves feed mostly on seeds, fruit, berries, and a few insects. Their wings are strong and pointed, making for powerful flight. This is vital for some species, who have to travel miles to obtain food for their young. The body is small and compact, with the pectoral muscles well developed. The feathers are weakly attached and will fall off very easily.

One of the possibilities for the "dove" of Scripture is the common Rock Dove of Eurasia (*Columba livia*), commonly known as the Domestic or Street Pigeon. This bird has always been close to man, highly regarded both for its ability to learn to carry messages and for the tastiness of its flesh. There are nearly 200 known varieties within this species, thanks to 5000 years of selective breeding by man.

The true doves (*Turtur*) which are undoubtedly those usually referred to in the Bible, inhabit Eurasia, Africa, Australia, and the Indo-

Malayan region. They are smaller than the street pigeon and have longer tails. They are mostly gray or buff in color, with a blackish or checkered half-collar on the back of the neck. Pure white domestic breeds have been developed. The birds of this group also lay only 2 eggs. The nest is built of twigs gathered by the female. Incubation lasts 17 days and is performed by the female. The male feeds the female on the nest. The young leave the nest about 3 weeks after hatching, but still receive some parental care for a few more days. Courtship is taken very seriously, and there is a great deal of rivalry among the males. The courtship dance is an awesome aerial display.

THE CUCKOO-LIKE BIRDS (*Cuculiformes*)

This is a small assemblage of really very odd birds with remarkable habits—the turacos or plantain eaters of the tropics; the anis; the roadrunners; the coucals; and the true cuckoos. Even the last are themselves remarkably varied.

THE CUCKOO FAMILY (*Cuculidae*)

The cuckoos are a universally distributed group of birds that exhibit great variety in form and habits. Some build nests, others are parasitic. The family is distinguished by having a zygodactyle foot and a naked oil gland. The body feathers lack any trace of aftershafts. There are usually 10 tail feathers, although in one group only 8 are present. Some 130 species of cuckoos proper are now recognized.

58. *Cuckoo*

"But these *are they* of which ye shall not eat . . . the night hawk, and the cuckow, and the hawk after his kind" (Deut. 14:12, 15).

"And these *are they which* ye shall have in abomination among the fowls; they shall not be eaten, they *are* an abomination; the eagle, and the ossifrage, and the ospray . . . And the owl, and the night hawk, and the cuckow, and the hawk after his kind . . ." (Lev. 11:13, 16).

The Hebrew *shachaph*, which is generally taken to be the cuckoo, appears only twice in the Bible, in the lists of unclean birds in Leviticus and Deuteronomy—relegated there most probably because it was considered to feed carnivorously. Thirty-seven species of true cuckoos (*Cuculinae*) are found in the Old World. They vary considerably in size and participate in a highly organized form of nesting behavior. Cuckoos lay their eggs in the nests of other birds, and then delude the owners of the nest into fostering their young.

In contrast to some brilliantly colored species, the true cuckoo is brownish above, with spotted brown and gray under parts. The tail is graduated and the bill is quite large. Cuckoos feed chiefly on insects but some also take lizards, frogs, snakes, and young birds. Cuckoos are quite proficient in the art of deception. A number of species imitate hawks, sunbirds, and even ravens. The imitations involve modification of plumage, calls, and actions. Their technique of camouflage is incredibly detailed. This ability is a source of considerable confusion to many bird watchers.

The cuckoo referred to in the Bible is the *Cuculus canorus,* or the Common European Cuckoo. It resembles a hawk in the shape of its body. The species consists of a number of populations which seem identical to each other but which consistently lay differently colored eggs. Some lay eggs which are blue, and parasitize birds that lay bluish eggs; others lay eggs that are buff with black spots, and parasitize birds that lay eggs of the same coloration. This kind of intraspecific variation contains many important implications for the study of the evolution of species.

The egg which the cuckoo leaves in the foster nest usually has detrimental effects on the foster bird's own young, since the parasitized bird is usually a member of a smaller and weaker species. The intruding young often will get under the legitimate young and heave them over the rim of the nest. As a result, the parasite manages to obtain for itself all of the food brought by its foster parents.

Many cuckoos migrate as far as several thousand miles in order to take advantage of the sources of insect food which shift with the seasons. The parents leave their eggs in nests of other birds and proceed to migrate; the young catch up to and rejoin their parents about a month later.

The Great Spotted Cuckoo (*Clamator glandarius*) is frequently seen in Palestine but confined to the northern and central regions. It consistently lays its eggs in the nests of the Hooded Crow, which nourishes the foster young with mice and carrion.

THE OWLS (*Strigiformes*)

Due mainly to their "owl face," the members of the owl group are easily distinguished from all other birds. The face is large in relation to the rest of the body, and the eyes point forward instead of to the side, as in most other birds. Around the eyes are circular disks of radiating feathers, which may, in turn, be bounded by a ruff of closely set feathers. Many owls have tufts or crests of feathers above the eyes commonly known as "ears." In keeping with their role as birds of prey, all owls are equipped with a short, stout, strongly curved beak and sharp, curved claws.

THE TRUE OWL FAMILY (*Strigidae*)

The Family *Strigidae* is characterized by a breastbone with a complete lower margin, and by a keel firmly united to the furcula. The inner edge of the third claw is serrated, while the third and second toes are of equal length. There are a large number of species distributed almost worldwide. The Barn or Monkey-faced Owls form a separate family— the *Tytonidae*.

59. Owl

"Therefore the wild beasts of the desert, with the wild beasts of the islands, shall dwell *there*, and the owls shall dwell therein: and it shall be no more inhabited for ever: neither shall it be dwelt in from generation to generation" (Jer. 50:39).

There are several different types of owl mentioned in the Bible. Owing to etymological confusion, the exact number is uncertain. Several translations of the Bible render the Hebrew word *bath-haya'anah* as "owl," but Tristram argues that, in these places (Job 30:29, Isa. 13:21, Isa. 34:13, Isa. 43:20, Jer. 50:39, Mic. 1:8, and in the lists of unclean birds), a more proper rendering should read "ostrich"! (*See* OSTRICH, page 136.) Another Hebrew word, *yanshooph*, occurs in the unclean birds list as well as in Isaiah, which reads, "And the owl and the raven shall dwell therein," referring to the downfall of Edom. The owl noted there probably refers to the Egyptian Eagle Owl, a large bird which nests in abandoned ruins.

Another owl, signified by the Hebrew word *cos*, appears in the unclean birds list, and is mentioned in Psalm 102. "I am like the owl of the desert," seems to indicate the Little Owl (*Athene noctua*), which is the most common of the several species that dwell in the Biblical lands. Another owl, the Hebrew *kippoz*, is mentioned by Isaiah as a future dweller in the ruins of Edom (Isa. 34:15). The *kippoz* is the very small (about 7 inches long) Scops Owl (*Otus scops*) which, like the Egyptian Eagle Owl, makes its home in the ruins that dot the Biblical landscape.

In the same passage, describing the downfall of Edom we have already mentioned, a marginal note in Isaiah, referring to the "screech owl," speaks of a "night-monster" that "shall repose there" (Isa. 34:14). The Hebrew word for the night-monster is *lilith*. The word is also the name of the first wife of Adam, who appears in apocryphal versions of the Creation, where it is told that she refused to obey Adam and was driven out of Eden. She later became an Assyrian goddess of the night and protector of demons. Jewish folklore records how in the night she would swoop down upon sleeping children and carry them away. The only use of the word *lilith* is in the Isaiah passage cited above, where most translators render it as "night-monster." A naturalistic equivalent of *lilith* may connote a bird, most probably an owl, specifically the Hooting or Tawny Owl (*Stryx aluco*) common in many parts of the Near East. Correlating evidence is the Jewish folklore superstition that owls attack sleeping children at night, tearing at their faces with their claws.

There are 133 species of owls scattered around the world. They vary considerably in size; some of them are as small as sparrows, others as large as roosters. They feed on arthropods, fish, amphibians, birds, and small mammals. They obtain their food mostly at night. The owl pounces on its prey with its strong legs and sharp, powerful claws. The eyes of the owl are specially devised for its nocturnal existence. This ability to see so well at night is the characteristic which most people tend to associate with the owl; what is usually overlooked is the fact that the ears of the owl are just as well accommodated. Because of their keen hearing, many species are able to attack prey successfully in absolute darkness. The shape of the bird's head is modified in accordance with the enlarged eyes and ears.

The face of the owl is usually flattened. It is covered with feathers that have a hard, wiry texture, and radiate outward from the beak and eyes to form a disklike structure. This peculiar arrangement may help the owl to see and hear better. The owl's bill is markedly hooked. Near the bill are the nostrils, and above them the eyes. The eyes are directed forward and cannot be turned in their sockets. To compensate for this, the owl is capable of twisting his head and neck in a strange and peculiar manner, rotating it through 270 degrees or more. The plumage is usually soft. The edges of the flight feathers are tipped with delicate filaments which serve to eliminate practically all the noise when the bird is flying. The wings are short and rounded, and the tail is short and square.

Owls are noted for making weird noises. This is one of the reasons why they have long been regarded as ill omens. These sounds are prevalent during the courting season. The eerie cries serve as a means of attracting a mate. At times the male and female join in together to make a very strange woodland concert. The eggs of owls are round and white. The number deposited varies from 1 to 12, depending on the species. As a rule, the farther north the habitations of the bird are, the greater the number of eggs deposited, so that the owls of the Arctic produce the largest number of eggs.

Most of the small- and medium-sized owls nest in cavities in trees or in the ground. Some of the large owls nest on the open tundras or in nests constructed from grass and feathers. A few species prefer grassy swamps. The unusual phenomenon of "staggered birth" can be witnessed among owls. In this, incubation begins right after the first egg has been laid. Other eggs are deposited while the incubation is taking place. The result is that a young owl hatches while its brothers and sisters are still under incubation. The incubation period varies from 25 to 35 days, according to the species. Owls are very courageous in defending their young against danger. At the time the baby owls hatch, they are covered with a thick white down. Owl nests are easy to detect because the owls litter the surrounding ground with parts of their prey, such as heads and wings. Owls begin to hunt at late dusk. Some hunt in the grasslands of swamps, while others frequent forests. Some species are migratory.

One of the famous Biblical species is the Short-eared Owl (*Asio flammeus*), which is found over most of the Northern Hemisphere. The bird is 15 inches in length. It frequents grassy swamps, building nests from the grass by the water. It eats insects and small rodents. In winter it may roost in groups on the ground. The so-called Owlet (*Athene noctua*) is one of the most familiar owls inhabiting Eurasia. The genus received its name from Athena, the Greek goddess of wisdom. The Owlet is seen by day as well as by night, and breeds in all countries bordering on the Mediterranean.

The Screech or Scops Owls are also an interesting group. They are smallish birds, found almost everywhere throughout the world. One of the species (*Otus scops*) is a well-known inhabitant of Eurasia and Africa. Another species is the *Otus asio*, whose members exhibit a wide variety of coloration. The inhabitants of moist areas are somewhat blackish, while the desert dwellers are much lighter in color. Screech Owls are famous for their whistling calls which resound through the night. They feed on insects and small mammals and birds, and will attack a man if he intrudes on their nests.

The Barn Owl (*Tyto alba*), often erroneously called Screech Owl, is almost worldwide in range and is found in Palestine.

EXOTIC BIRDS (*Coraciiformes*)

This is in some respects a sort of catch-all, but the numerous families of birds included in the Order do show certain anatomical relationships. Included in it are the kingfishers, todies, and motmots; the bee-eaters and the rollers; the hornbills; and the hoopoes. While bee-eaters and rollers are known from Palestine, the ancients did not see fit to mention them specifically. The hoopoe, perhaps because of its odd and colorful appearance and rather nasty habits, they did.

THE HOOPOE FAMILY (*Upupidae*)

The hoopoes are beautiful, desert-dwelling birds distinguished by the sandy hue of their plumage and the squared form of their tail. They are further characterized by rounded, open nostrils and a bridged structure of the palate. There is a large perforation in the forepart of the breastbone which allows the metacoracoid bones to meet at the middle line.

60. Hoopoe

The Hoopoe is probably the bird indicated by the Hebrew word *dukipath*, which appears among the lists of unclean birds in Leviticus and Deuteronomy. It may hold its place there as much because it was held in religious reverence by the Egyptians, as because of its rather dirty feeding and nesting habits. The Hoopoe derives its name from the singular sound of its resounding call. To emit the sound, the neck feathers are puffed out and the head is snapped in the air. If on the ground, the bird hammers its beak into the earth.

The Hoopoe is an extremely attractive bird, closely related to the hornbill, though different from it in appearance. It is highly ornamented, with a tall and expansive crest of feathers on the top of its head. When the bird is alarmed, these feathers are erected. The bird is a beautiful salmon pink, and the feathers on its back, wings and tail resemble in their coloration the hide of a zebra. The legs and tail are short and the toes are separated. The bill is relatively long and delicately curved. The bird is not afraid of humans, permitting them to approach very close to it. It is about 12 inches long.

Hoopoes inhabit a variety of open and partially open areas in the warmer sections of the Old World, ranging from semiarid regions to public parks. Some hoopoes are migratory. In the summer they may appear in such distant places as Iceland, Japan, and Finland.

The Hoopoe feeds on worms, caterpillars, spiders, beetles, crickets, and many other invertebrates, often drilling its beak into the ground to help it obtain the food. Hoopoes usually hunt alone or in pairs during the breeding season. At other times they travel in small groups. The nest consists of a hole in a tree, house, or even anthill. The Hoopoe does very little to improve the nest once it has been selected. It lays from 4 to 8 eggs, which are basically blue to white in color.

The female performs all of the incubating, a task which lasts about 2 weeks. During this period a special oil gland at the base of her tail becomes active. This is a good means of defense for herself and her young. The secretion is a dirty blackish brown fluid the odor of which is so intense as to discourage any invader. While she is performing the incubation, she is fed on the nest by the male. The young do not leave the nest until about a month after hatching. Some of the food procured by the male is used to nourish the young. Later on, the male feeds the young himself. The recently hatched young are naked, but soon develop a covering of down and sharp blue quills. When they leave the nest they are colored like the adults. It takes about a year for their bills to develop to full size.

In Israel, the Hoopoe is seen in the northern and central parts only. They are useful birds, since they devour grubs, insects, and mole crickets. The bird is a summer breeder, arriving in February and leaving in September. It was considered an unclean animal by the Hebrews because of its habit of probing in filth for insects and worms.

THE SONG BIRDS (*Passeriformes*)

This Order includes the majority of birds, and is well represented over most of the world. Included within this Order are the group popularly known as song birds. All are characterized by the production of their young in a helpless and nearly naked state, most having only scattered patches of down over the body. They are often referred to as "perching birds," for the first toe is mobile and directed backward, and is capable of being worked independently of the other digits. The legs are covered with feathers as far down as the ankle. The number of primary quills in the wings varies from 9 to 10, and there are usually 12 feathers in the tail.

THE CROW FAMILY (*Corvidae*)

The *Corvidae* includes the crows, ravens, magpies, jays, and rooks, all of which are easily distinguished although they have few characteristics in common. All possess strong, large beaks which lack a distinct notch in the upper mandible. The toes are normal, but the first is shorter than the third. The nostrils in most cases are protected by a number of stiff bristles that reach halfway down the beak. The wing always has 10 quills, and the tail, 12 feathers.

61. Raven

"And these *are they which* ye shall have in abomination among the fowls; they shall not be eaten, they *are* an abomination; the eagle, and the ossifrage, and the ospray, And the vulture, and the kite after his kind; Every raven after his kind . . ." (Lev. 11:13–15).

"His head *is as* the most fine gold; his locks *are* bushy, *and* black as a raven" (Song of Sol. 5:11).

The Raven (*Corvus corax*) is the largest member of the family. The bill is somewhat cone-shaped, and the base of the upper "jaw" is usually covered with fine, wiry feathers. These birds eat all kinds of food, including carrion, insects, seeds, fruits, reptilian eggs, avian eggs, and small reptiles. They are crafty and active animals, widely known for their remarkable intelligence. Some are capable of "speaking," solving puzzles, and performing feats of "memory." They are bold, curious birds, and sometimes use their talents for theft. Ravens are found all over the world. Another well-known member of the group is the Black-billed Magpie (*Pica pica*) which is found throughout the Northern Hemisphere. The

Biblical "raven" might, in some cases, be the variety *Pica pica bactriana*. It is about 20 inches in length.

It may seem strange that the crow is not mentioned in the Bible more especially since the species found in the area is a rather striking bird— the Hooded Crow. However, the name *oreb* would appear to have covered the whole family.

THE SWALLOW FAMILY (*Hirundinidae*)

This group possesses a short, wide, and deeply cleft bill. The wings are very long and narrow, and consist of only 9 primary quills. The tail is generally forked and contains 12 feathers. The feet are small and weak, and are poorly adapted for walking.

There are 74 recognized full species of swallows and their relatives the martins spread all over the world. These birds form a very close-knit family with very similar habits, for they are insect-eaters supreme. Many are of exquisite colors, displaying metallic sheens of greens, blues, bronzes, and coppers. Like the bats of the night, the swallows of the daylight hours have kept a constant check on airborne insects since time immemorial, and, without them, man would have been in a sorry state before the discovery of insecticides. Further, several members of the family have taken to associating with man, building their nests on and in his houses, barns, and other buildings, and gathering around his drinking ponds, lakes, and reservoirs. In many countries the association of men and swallows is almost symbiotic, for man, by his works, brings a plethora of insects which the birds then live on.

62. Swallow

"Yea, the stork in the heaven knoweth her appointed times; and the turtle and the crane and the swallow observe the time of their coming; but my people know not the judgment of the LORD" (Jer. 8:7).

"Yea, the sparrow hath found an house, and the swallow a nest for herself, where she may lay her young, *even* thine altars, O LORD of hosts, my King, and my God" (Ps. 84:3).

The *a-geor* of the Hebrews probably indicated any swallow-like bird but doubtless had special reference to the common House or Barndoor Swallow (*Hirundo rustica*) which has an almost universal range in the Northern Hemisphere. This beautiful and delicate little bird with its enchanting twitterings appealed greatly to all the ancients as a symbol of home life, gentility, and aesthetic fragility. Further, its ways were a great mystery to early peoples on account of its sudden and clockwork-like migrations or disappearances and reappearances, so that until quite recently it was believed that they hibernated in mud at the bottom of ponds during the winter.

THE FINCH FAMILY (*Fringillidae*)

The *Fringillidae* include a large number of small, hard-billed, seed-eating birds, such as the finches, sparrows, canaries, buntings, and cardinals. All have conical beaks characterized by the smooth edges of the mandibles. Of the 9 primary quills of the wing, the first and second are of equal length. The tail has 12 feathers and the sexes are usually unlike in size and coloring.

63. *Sparrow*

"I watch, and am as a sparrow alone upon the house top. Mine enemies reproach me all the day; *and* they that are mad against me are sworn against me. For I have eaten ashes like bread, and mingled my drink with weeping, Because of thine indignation and thy wrath: for thou hast lifted me up, and cast me down" (Ps. 102:7–10).

"Therefore I say unto you, Take no thought for your life, what ye shall eat, or what ye shall drink; nor yet for your body, what ye shall put on. Is not the life more than meat, and the body than raiment? Behold the fowls of the air: for they sow not, neither do they reap, nor gather into barns; yet your heavenly Father feedeth them. Are ye not much better than they?" (Matt. 6:25–26).

The appearance of the sparrow in the Bible is clouded by etymological confusion. The Hebrew word *tsippor* would be used to designate the sparrow, but it also is used for many different kinds of small birds, including wrens, thrushes, etc. Therefore, with few exceptions, *tsippor* is translated in most versions of the Bible to read "bird," thus becoming a generic term, rather than "sparrow," which would be more limiting. In Psalm 84, one of these exceptions appears. It reads: "Yea, the sparrow hath found an house, and the swallow a nest for herself, where she may lay her young, *even* thine altars, O Lord of hosts, my King and my God" (Ps. 84:3).

Sparrows are found in practically every section of the world. They practice solitary nesting and possess a tenth primary feather that is variable. The exact species to which the Bible refers is difficult to determine. One possibility is the *Fringilla patronia*. The members of the genus *Fringilla* are widely distributed throughout the Old World and migrate in unbelievably large hordes. In 1951, approximately 72 million members of one species of *Fringilla* entered Switzerland to roost.

Another possibility for the Biblical reference is the House Sparrow (*Passer domesticus*) which belongs to the *Ploceidae*, a family of birds famous for the complexity and size of their communal nests. The members of this family are commonly referred to as "weaverbirds." Some sparrow-sized members build nests that are as large as tents. Others build them with a delicacy that humans would find difficult to duplicate.

The common, so-called, English House Sparrow is a member of this family but has taken to solitary nesting for the most part. Most weavers have short, sturdy, conical bills. They are primarily arboreal, but search for food on the ground. Most species are nonmigratory. Some of these birds, like the cuckoos, have the ability to delude other birds into fostering their young. The *Ploceidae* are placed at the top of the evolutionary line because of the remarkable variety of specialization and adaptation found in the family. The genus *Passer* is probably the most famous of the weaverbirds. The House Sparrow thrives best in a human environment and now inhabits North America and all of Eurasia. It was introduced into North America in 1851.

Also occurring in Palestine is *Passer moabiticus,* or the Dead Sea Sparrow. It is a summer breeder, found only in the southern part of the Jordan Valley, around the shores of the Dead Sea. In the winter this bird migrates, but it is not yet known where it goes. The bird builds a large conical nest from the needles of the tamarisk. Eggs are laid from April to July. The bird feeds on seeds and insects.

Chapter 9

Reptiles, Amphibians, and Fish

REPTILES

THE SNAKES (Order, *Serpentes*)

Serpents belong to what is called a superorder of the reptiles known as the *Squamata*, which includes the lizards (Order, *Lacertilia*) and the snakes (Order, *Serpentes*). The snakes differ from lizards most notably in being able to swallow animals several times their own diameter. This is made possible by an unusually flexible jaw mechanism. Other distinguishing features are the absence of movable eyelids, of a middle ear cavity, and of legs. It is believed that snakes evolved from some primitive lizard group, probably from burrowing members which eventually lost their legs. Some snakes gave up the burrowing habit and developed a method of locomotion that depended upon squirming and the accompanying movement of ventral scales. Snakes are regarded as a very successful biological group, having undergone considerable evolutionary change.

Like lizards, snakes shed their worn skins periodically. Most lay eggs, and most embryo snakes have a special device to break open their shells, called "egg teeth," with which they slit the shell from the inside. Snakes have no eyelids so that their eyes are always open, enabling them when asleep to be "awakened" by seeing a moving object. They have no external ears and the internal ears are degenerate. Their main "hearing" apparatus is their long, slender tongues, which have a very sensitive

173

nerve system able to record, it is now believed, both airborne vibrations and possibly infrared (heat) waves.

64. Vipers (Adder)

"Dan shall be a serpent by the way, an adder in the path, that biteth the horse heels, so that his rider shall fall backward" (Gen. 49:17).

"He shall suck the poison of asps: the viper's tongue shall slay him" (Job 20:16).

"And when Paul had gathered a bundle of sticks, and laid *them* on the fire, there came a viper out of the heat, and fastened on his hand" (Acts 28:3).

The snake referred to here is now thought to be the Horned Viper (*Cerastes cerastes*). The older books have this snake classified as *Cerastes hasselquistii*, a desert species with a very toxic venom. It is relatively small, about a foot to 18 inches long, and as pale and sandy as the desert it thrives in. Over each eye there is a sharp, upright spine which gives it the name of the horned or arrow snake. They hide in the sand, in depressions such as those made by the hoofs of camels or horses, and if a man or some animal steps into such a hollow the snake strikes. It is supposed to strike sometimes without provocation, and its venom can kill in half an hour, making it as deadly as a cobra. Tristram believes this to be the "asp" that killed Cleopatra.

There is also a representative of a closely allied genus of snakes in Palestine. This is known as the False Viper or *Pseudocerastes fieldi*, a vicious little true desert species with valves inside its nostrils to seal them against the ultra-fine grains of sandstorms.

Because these are desert animals, their ribs are greatly flattened so they will not sink easily into the sand. They have also developed a good method for fast movement in the sand. The slow, forward progress of a viper is actually not a glide, but, closely watched, will be seen to consist of a movement of the ribs beneath the skin which might be compared to a centipede clad in the skin of a serpent and using its limbs in walking fashion. It is interesting to note that though snakes do not have legs, some can glide with the speed of a running man. This they accomplish by using the small declivities and projections on the ground as points from which they push off to gain speed. Their natural movements on the ground also enable nearly all serpents to swim gracefully and fast.

The word "viper" can refer to a large number of different kinds of snakes of the family *Viperidae*, all of which are poisonous. The Family is divided into a number of genera, one of which is *Vipera*, which is characterized by the presence of scales on the head that are of nearly the same size and type as those of the upper part of the body. The Adder of Europe (*Vipera berus*) is a member of this genus; and ranges from

England to Korea and Sakhalin. Closely related, but not to be confused with the Horned Viper (*Cerastes*) is (*V. ammodytes*) the Nose-horned Viper. It measures less than 2 feet, and is characterized by a small horn arising from the tip of the snout. It lies low in the sand, biting the heels of whatever mammal may dare to trespass. The color is gray, giving it excellent camouflage. The Hebrew word for viper is *akshub* or "coiling back," apparently derived from the characteristic posture of the animal. The bite is extremely toxic, causing swelling and almost immediate death in the victim. Another member of the same genus is the Palestine Viper (*Vipera palestina*). This snake possesses a neck which distends in the same way that the cobra's does. It is green in color, marked obliquely with brown bands. The length varies from 3 to 5 feet. Its bite allegedly brings instant and almost painless death. For this reason it became a highly preferred method of suicide, and, were it available, a much more likely candidate for Cleopatra's asp.

The name "adder" is an English equivalent of viper, used for the viper of the British Isles.

65. Asp (Cobra)

The word "asp" is derived from the Greek *aspis* which meant any poisonous snake. In old English it could, at one time, denote any snake from the region of Egypt or north Africa. However, there is now little doubt that it denotes, in the English translations of the Bible, the Egyptian Cobra (*Naja haje*), still another snake that has been named as the one that killed Cleopatra. It conceals itself in holes in walls and rocks, and has the power to expand its neck by raising its anterior ribs so as to dilate the front of its breast into the shape of a flat disk. When alarmed, it rises up with its neck spread out in this fashion, and attacks. In this pose it is depicted on ancient Egyptian monuments, where it represented immortality. The Egyptians looked upon it as a sacred creature. Since it fed on the rodents which ate the Egyptians' crops, it seemed to be a protector, to the Egyptians. As one early historian put it:

"One of the early Egyptian beliefs was that there first existed great silent darkness everywhere and that out of this great primordial night there evolved the world egg which eventually divided into the skies and the earth. Among the most common tradition is the one that ascribes to the Great World Serpent the warming and hatching of the egg, a phenomenon that has been commonly illustrated." (Henry B. Tristram, *Natural History of the Bible*)

The Egyptians also thought that the eclipses of the sun were due to the attacks upon the sun god Ra by the great serpent Apopi who lived in a celestial river. The sun was supposed to be the ship of Ra which passed across the sky, and when attacked by the serpent it was concealed by the fighting that was going on. *Naja haje* is dull brown, with short fangs which are stout and always erect on the forward part of the jaw.

African cobras are noted for the fact that some are able to spit their venom. They do not actually spit, but eject a spray for a considerable distance. The venom is pushed through the fangs by very strong muscles around the gland and is assisted forward by the forcible exhalation of air from the mouth. The spitting cobras usually shoot for the eyes, probably attracted by the white of the eye. The blindness and soreness of the eyes then give the snake an opportunity to escape. Complete blindness does not usually but sometimes does occur. It is invariably painful.

THE LIZARDS (Order, *Sauria*)

Although most lizards can easily be distinguished by their four-limbed body divided into definite head, neck, trunk, and tail, some forms have lost all external trace of limbs, and therefore closely resemble the snakes. In all true lizards, however, the two sections of the lower jaw are joined at the chin by a bony structure. The species equipped with limbs have definite collarbones, and even where the limbs have been lost some traces of these still persist. The tongue is flattened, and can never be withdrawn into a basal sheath, as is the case with snakes.

The Order *Sauria* is a vast one, and is spread all over the world from northern temperate to southern temperate latitudes. It is divided into a great number of genera and 19 Families. Members of at least 4 of these are mentioned in the Bible, but in each case the identification of the animal is not decisive, while there are also grave doubts as to the correctness of the translation of the Hebrew names involved. Even the Greeks were unaware of all but 3 of the Families, and the English translators knew only of one.

66. *Lizard*

This Family—the typical lizards (Family, *Lacertidae*)—contains numerous genera, and is spread all over Eurasia and most of Africa. The type-genus is *Lacerta*, which comprises the commonest lizards of Europe where animals were first classified. In a passage from Leviticus (Lev. 11:29–30), quoted in full later, a clear distinction is made between what appear to be three reptiles: the ferret (*see* GECKO, below), the chameleon, and the lizard. The Hebrew words involved are *anakah*, *tinshemeth*, and *cho-met*, respectively. (The first two are discussed later.)

Several species of lizards, including more than one species of *Lacerta*, are found in Palestine, occupying various environments, and there can be no doubt that the Hebrews knew the animals well. That lizards crawled upon their bellies would make them unclean, and that the *cho-met* is associated with two other lizard types in this passage makes the identification almost certain. However, whether any specific lizard, lacertid or otherwise, was meant or whether the title was a general one for all lizards other than the chameleon and gecko, cannot be determined. Some scholars have inclined to the view that another group of lizards known as the skinks (Family *Scincidae*), creatures that burrow and members of which are also found in the area, was intended, but there is no direct evidence for this.

67. The Chameleon

Chameleons are a unique and highly specialized group of four-legged reptiles. The compressed body, short, thin neck, and slender, elongated limbs give them an appearance much different from that of the true lizards. They are possessed of a long, wormlike tongue, the end of which is thickened and covered with a viscous substance. This organ can be quickly extended to trap any insect passing within several inches of the mouth. The feet are characterized by toes divided into two opposing branches of two each, thus forming powerful grasping organs. Aided further by a long prehensile tail, which acts as a fifth hand, the chameleons are well adapted for their life among the branches of trees and shrubs. The structure of the eye presents another outstanding peculiarity of the group. A minute pupil is located in the center of a large eyeball otherwise covered by granular skin, and each eyeball can move independently of its mate to focus on a given object. Chameleons further differ from the true lizards in having no collarbones, and in having the scales of the head and body replaced by granules.

The chameleon is a reptile that is common in the Holy Land. These animals have such enormous lungs that ancient peoples thought they lived on air. When they fill their lungs with air they supposedly become semitransparent. They also have the ability to change color, though this is not as well developed in them as it is in several other animals— notably the octopus. These color changes occur not only according to the variability of shade or background, but also with changes in the temperature, and in their emotions. Though chameleons feed primarily on insects, one larger species is alleged to feed on mice, and another on birds! The largest species of all is over 2 feet long and is found in Madagascar.

68. Gecko (Ferret?)

"These also *shall be* unclean unto you among the creeping things that creep upon the earth; the weasel, and the mouse, and the tortoise after his kind, And the ferret, and the chameleon, and the lizard, and the snail, and the mole" (Lev. 11:29–30).

Almost all scholars agree that the ferret is not the animal intended by the Hebrew word *anakah*, since naturalists maintain that no ferrets were present in Palestine and Syria. Many of the Rabbinical writers translated *anakah* as "hedgehog." The Greek Septuagint translated the word as "shrew." Bible scholars point out that the literal meaning of *anakah* was "groaner" or "sigher." Since the creature was classed in a group of creeping things, many commentators believe that the animal intended was the gecko, popularly known as the wall lizard. The gecko makes a low, mourning sound by vibrating its tongue rapidly against the roof of its mouth. There also was a popular folk legend that a gecko would cause leprosy if it crawled across one's body. This folk belief naturally confirms the Hebrew conception that the animal was unclean.

The gecko was commonly found throughout the Holy Land. Being unclean, it would be a constant nuisance in a home, for it can walk upside down on ceilings and often plop down into the middle of the home. The Arabs of the present day are horribly frightened by the gecko, believing that it poisons all that it touches. It is much like the fear that the English and Americans feel toward the common toad, for both creatures, though repulsive in appearance, are quite harmless.

THE CROCODILIANS (Order, *Crocodilia*)

Including the alligators, gavials, caimans, and crocodiles, the members of the Order *Crocodilia* represent a very ancient and distinct group of reptiles. All are characterized by large, lizard-like bodies supported by short legs. Posteriorly the body develops into a long, highly compressed tail that is a great aid in swimming, serving both as a paddle and a rudder. The head terminates in a flattened snout armed with strong, conical teeth, each of which is implanted in a distinct socket. New teeth growing from beneath continually replace those in use. The fore-feet and hind-feet exhibit five and four toes, respectively. The toes are webbed, and the three innermost digits on each foot are equipped with stout claws. The back and tail of the beasts are protected by quadrangular horny shields of varying size. These are arranged in regular rows, and are in contact with one another at the edges. The ears are covered with movable lids which can be closed when the animal enters the water. *Crocodilia* are all able to breathe with their mouths open and filled with water, for the windpipe extends to a cavity located just behind the nostrils, which is entirely cut off from the mouth.

69. Crocodile

The Hebrew word *livyathan* appears only 5 times in the Bible, and not one of these references actually reveals the creature intended by the writers. The Jewish Bible, the Talmud, accepted the creature intended as being unquestionably the "crocodile." The general consensus is that the word *livyathan,* which means "mourning," is a term used figuratively to signify all the great creatures of the water. The Hebrew word has been variously translated as "a wreathed animal," "a twisted animal," and "one spirally wound." Some scholars have attempted to restrict its meaning to the whale, but it is more broadly accepted as a general term for all serpentine, cetacean, and saurian monsters of the sea. Isaiah used the word "leviathan" to mean "crooked serpent," apparently symbolizing Assyria, the dread enemy of the Israelites.

The crocodile is not known in Palestine but was plentiful in Egypt, where it must have been a commonplace to the Hebrews during their lengthy sojourn there. It would probably have been held in abomination by them as there was an Egyptian crocodile god.

AMPHIBIANS

THE FROGS (Order, *Salientia*)

As is the case with all amphibians, the frogs and toads are covered by a soft, hairless skin. They are distinguished from the other members of the Class by the presence of four limbs and the lack of a tail in the adult state. The hind-legs which are much longer and more powerfully developed than the fore-legs, enable the animals to jump large distances. Generally, most frogs and toads pass through an extended larval period. Known as tadpoles or pollywogs, the larvae have globular heads, gills, fishlike tails, and no limbs.

70. Frogs

"And the Lord spake unto Moses, Go unto Pharaoh, and say unto him, Thus saith the Lord, Let my people go, that they may serve me. And if thou refuse to let *them* go, behold, I will smite all thy borders with frogs: And the river shall bring forth frogs abundantly, which shall go up and come into thine house, and into thy bedchamber, and upon thy bed, and into the house of thy servants, and upon thy people, and into thine ovens, and into thy kneadingtroughs; And the frogs shall come up, both on thee, and upon thy people, and upon all thy servants" (Exod. 8:1–4).

Frogs are one of the commonest animals of Egypt, where they are found in great numbers in the marshes and along the waterways. To the Hebrews the frogs represented uncleanliness because of their somewhat slimy appearance, though the frog referred to in the Bible is probably the edible one, *Rana ridibunda.* This is one of the aquatic frogs found in Egypt and in the stagnant waters of the Holy Land. They abound in such numbers that visitors have reported that their croaking at night is deafening. The voice is primarily used by the male to call a mate. The females do not usually use their voices, and the females' vocal powers are small compared to that of the male. Croaking may also take place underwater where the air is forced from the lungs, past the vocal cords, into the mouth cavity and back again. Since they do much of their breathing through their skin, this does not seem to harm them.

These frogs hibernate in the mud in the bottoms of ponds, in springs, or in damp spots in the woods. This is in response to temperature. Their slipperiness is protective so that they can't be held. They are usually great leapers, and can also be "hypnotized" by placing them on their backs for a few moments. Their responses then become slowed and they show a sort of death faint.

FISH

71. Fish (General)

This class consists of a large, highly varied group of cold-blooded vertebrate animals that are completely adapted to aquatic life. The limbs and tail are modified into fins; along the medians there are unpaired fins supported by bony rays. With few exceptions, fish breathe solely by the use of gills. All of the higher groups are equipped with distinct jaws. The skin may be naked or covered with scales or bony plates.

Fishes are mentioned many times in the Bible under the general title *dag* and no attempt is made by its writers to distinguish between species or even groups of fish. The Hebrew nation was landlocked, the coast of Palestine being occupied by the Phoenicians, the Philistines, and the other "Sea Peoples," so that they had little knowledge of marine fish, while what we call generally "shellfish" were declared unclean. When the Hebrews were in Egypt they must have known many different kinds of fishes regularly taken from the Nile by the Egyptians, but when they settled in Israel, their acquaintance with fish was confined to those of the Jordan and Lake Galilee.

Mention of fish becomes much more frequent in the New Testament, and they played a rather prominent part in both early and medieval Christian symbolism, due probably to their forming the central theme of two of Christ's miracles.

Chapter 10

Other Animals of the Bible

INSECTS				
Hymenoptera	72. Bees	Devorah	*Apis mellifera*	
	73. Hornet	Tzir-or	*Vespa crabro*	
	74. Ants	Nemalah	(various)	
Lepidoptera	75. Moths	Awsh	(Notably Clothes Moths)	
	75. Caterpillars	Chasil	(Larvae of same)	
Diptera	76. Flies	Zevuv	Muscids of many kinds	
	77. Gnats	Parósh	*Simulium* spp.	
	77. Mosquitoes	(ditto ?)	*Culex* spp.	
Siphanaptera	78. Fleas	Yav-chus	*Pulex irritans*, and others	
Anoplura	79. Lice	Sciniphs	*Pediculus humanus*	
Orthoptera	80. Grasshoppers	Arbeh	(various)	
	80. Locusts	Chor-gorv	*Locusta migratoria, et al.*	

ARACHNIDS			
Araneae	81. Spiders	Akkabish	(various)
Scorpionida	82. Scorpions	Akrav	(various)

MOLLUSCS			
Gasteropoda	83. Snails	Shablul	(Land, freshwater, and marine).

WORMS			
Hirudinea	84. Leeches	Alukah	Specially *Haemopis sanguisuga*

ZOOPHYTES			
Coelenterata	85. Coral	Raw-maw	(various)

SPONGES			
Keratosa	86. Sponge	Is-vog	(various)

The Animal Kingdom is divided into two great parts: that of the single-celled animals (*Protozoa*) and the multicelled (*Metazoa*). We are concerned here with only the latter, for the existence of the former was not known to the writers of the Bible. The *Metazoa* are divided into a number of what are called "Phyla," but these are of very varying degrees of importance and numbers of forms. Currently, there are 26 recognized Phyla of which more than half were once lumped together simply as "worms!" The Bible mentions members of only 6 of these—the *Chordata*, or animals with backbones; the *Arthropoda*, or jointed-legged ones, the insects, arachnids, crustaceans, and their allies; the *Mollusca*, or snails and other shellfish; one form of the *Annelida* or segmented true worms; and, in general terms, the *Coelenterata* (coral), and the *Porifera* (sponges).

181

INSECTS

THE BEES, WASPS, AND ANTS (Order, *Hymenoptera*)

In terms of specialization of structure, the bees, wasps, and ants rank among the most highly developed of the insects. The body is divided into a distinct head, thorax, and abdomen, the last being attached to the thorax by a narrow stalk. Very often the hard, shiny exoskeleton is covered with hair. The mandibles are well adapted for biting, although in the case of the honeybees the mouth parts are modified into a tongue-like proboscis for sucking nectar from flowers. The legs are often armed with spines, and the wings, when present, are strong, light, and transparent. Always four in number, the upper and under wings on each side are attached to one another by a series of minute hooks on their adjacent margins. The abdomens of the females are often armed with either an instrument for boring or a powerful stinger. In all species metamorphosis is complete.

72. Bee

"And after a time he returned to take her, and he turned aside to see the carcase of the lion; and, behold, *there was* a swarm of bees and honey in the carcase of the lion" (Judg. 14:8).

Bees are plentiful in Palestine. They are the same species (*Apis mellifera*) that we have domesticated, but which, in Biblical times, were known only in the wild state. The wild bees of this region are especially noted for their ferocity in attack. The virulence of their venom increases in warm weather. They build their hives and nests on precipitous rocks or in hollow trees hard for man or animals to reach. Since there are few forests in the area they build mostly on rocks.

Even today much of the honey of this region is collected from these wild bees, though they attack man with a special fury because they are not used to humans. Some years ago the people of the region let a man down the face of the rocks by ropes. He wore protective clothing that completely shielded him from the attacks of the bees and gathered a large amount of honey. However, he was so intimidated by the great swarms of angry bees that he could not be persuaded to repeat the adventure.

The Bible quotation refers to the fact that a few hours after an animal's death the scavengers, such as jackals and vultures, reduce the carcass to the bone, and after the skeleton has dried in the sun, the bees find this an excellent place to start a new honeycomb.

Bees have a very complex social structure which centers around the queen bee. The fertilized queen lives through the winter. In the spring she lays a few eggs in a cavity and infertile female workers develop from some of the eggs. They carry on all of the activities of the colony except laying eggs. At the end of the summer, drones or males, and fertile females which will become queens, hatch from some of the eggs. These mate and the sperm receptacles of the queens are filled. The drones then die, and the race is maintained until the next fall by the queens alone.

The social structure varies with different types of bees. When an egg is laid its future is decided by its food. If a larva is fed "bee bread," an infertile female worker is the result. The drones are also fed on "bee bread." But if a larva is fed on "royal jelly," then this larva will eventually become a queen.

Since bees collect nectar, they have a system of communication to inform each other where the source is. Their main method of talking to each other depends on rhythmic movements, and on odors, but it has recently been discovered that they do also employ a "language" based on sound. A bee informs others of a source of nearby nectar by means of a round dance in which it turns around first one way and then another. This dance gives no indication of direction except to indicate that the nectar is close by. The specific odor of the plant visited, which is on the body of the informing bee, tells her companions the kind of flower to search for. If food is farther away than about 165 to 330 feet, the round dance is replaced by the tail-wagging dance. This not only tells the source of food and odor, but also the distance and direction in which it will be found. As the distance between the feeding place and hive increases, the tail-wagging dance decreases. The direction of the head in a short straight run indicates the direction of the nectar source in relation to the sun. The dances are closely watched by the other bees, who then go out to gather the nectar.

Bees are sensitive to color, being able to distinguish four: blue-green, yellow-green, blue-violet, and ultraviolet. Ultraviolet is invisible to man.

73. *Hornet*

"I will send my fear before thee, and will destroy all the people to whom thou shalt come; and I will make all thine enemies turn their backs unto thee. And I will send hornets before thee, which shall drive out the Hivite, the Canaanite, and the Hittite, from before thee" (Exod. 23:27–28).

The hornets belong to the wasp Family, with four species found in the Holy Land. These have vicious stings and can drive cattle and horses to madness, even death, by their attacks. The name "hornet" applies in Europe to a large species (*Vespa crabro*) of what we in America call a Yellow Jacket; the Yellow Jacket is called, in English, simply the

"Wasp." In America, the name "hornet" is applied to a number of other Hymenopterous insects related to the wasps proper. *Vespa crabro* has been introduced into North America.

74. Ants

Ants are found all over the world, from the burning deserts of Arabia to the rims of the polar icecaps. Naturally, then, men of Biblical times saw and studied these little creatures, and, as they often did, drew from the lives of the ants a moral lesson. To the ancient Hebrews, ants embodied two great virtues, industry and wisdom, and they used ants to represent both of these qualities in the Book of Proverbs.

One of the most famous of the proverbs involves the ant: "Go to the ant, thou sluggard; consider her ways, and be wise":

The illustration of this homily following these two lines is less well known: "Which [i.e., the ant] having no chief, overseer, or ruler, provideth her bread in the summer; *and* gathereth her food in the harvest" (Prov. 6:6–8).

The other proverb involving the ant is less well known, the reason most likely being that, while we still think of ants as industrious, somehow we no longer consider them particularly wise: "There are four *things which are* little upon the earth, but they *are* exceeding wise: the ants *are* a people not strong, yet they provide their food in the summer" (Prov. 30:24–25).

(The other animals mentioned by Proverbs in this connection, incidentally, are rock-badgers, locusts, and spiders.)

The basis for these proverbs is that the ant stores up food in the summer for use during the wintertime. In olden days, this notion was quite widespread, and it appears not only in the Bible but also in the folklore of many peoples. The famous story of the ant and the grasshopper says much the same thing as these proverbs.

This belief, however, has little basis in fact. In climates where there is a true winter, the ants, when the weather turns cold, enter a state of dormancy similar to the hibernation of higher animals; in this state they do not eat. In tropical climes, where winter never comes, the activity of the ant continues all year round and, obviously, there is no need to store food. Furthermore, the food of most ants consists of other insects and animals and the sap from trees, materials which could not be stored anyway.

How, then, did the belief that the ants store food arise? The answer is quite simple. It must have been a common enough experience for the Hebrews to see ants carrying bits of grain, leaves, and other matter to their nest. The ants' work never seemed to cease, and the ancients undoubtedly marveled at how diligently these little creatures went about their appointed tasks. Probably they broke open the ants' nests on occasion and found there quantities of grain and chaff. The simple assumption was that, like men, ants collect a harvest in the fall and store it up for the winter. This, after all, was the only way of life the Hebrews knew. The truth is, though, that the ants were not using these things to eat; they were simply lining their nests with them to make them dry and snug.

There are those who disagree with this interpretation of the Biblical passages, and naturalists have discovered that at least three species of ants, all common to the Mediterranean area, actually do store their food for the winter. In any case, the ant is one of nature's busiest and most organized creatures, and thus was an apt example for the writer of Proverbs.

The Moths and Butterflies (Order, *Lepidoptera*)

Composed of the butterflies and moths, the Order *Lepidoptera* contains some of the most beautiful of all insects. They are distinguished from other insects by the presence of four large wings covered with tiny, exquisitely shaped scales. Actually the scales are modified hairs that are broadened and flattened to cover the delicate membrane of the wing. A few butterflies and moths lack these scales and so exhibit clear wings. The usual insect jaws are replaced by a long, tubular proboscis that is used to draw honey from flowers or other juices, as some are carrion or dung feeders. All members undergo metamorphosis in their development. From the eggs hatch free-living larvae called caterpillars, which eventually develop into a quiescent pupa stage, and from there into a fully formed adult. The larvae have powerful jaws and feed on leaves and other fibers, both plant and animal.

75. Moths

"And he, as a rotten thing, consumeth, as a garment that is moth eaten" (Job 13:28).

"Behold, the Lord God will help me; who *is* he *that* shall condemn me? lo, they all shall wax old as a garment; the moth shall eat them up" (Isa. 50:9).

Clothes moth larvae are intended in the verse, not the actual adult moth. Damage to clothing is caused by these small white caterpillars. The moths belong to the Family *Tineidae*, with several small moths capable of damaging clothing. The most common of these is *Tinea bisseliela*, which formerly was known as *Tinea pellionella*. These are small yellowish insects with narrow, fringed wings.

THE TWO-WINGED FLIES (Order, *Diptera*)

The flies form a group that is distinguished from most other insects by the presence of a single pair of wings.* Usually these are naked, but they may, as in the mosquitoes, be furnished with short hairs. The mouth parts are formed for piercing and sucking, the mandibles being modified into a pair of sharp lancets. The ends of the legs are armed with two claws, and are also usually equipped with adhesive pads, which enable the insects to walk on smooth vertical surfaces. Like most other insects, flies undergo a complete metamorphosis. In the larval stage they are known as maggots.

76. Flies

There are many types of flies in the Palestine region, but the flies probably referred to are *Musca domestica*, the Common House Fly. However, most likely flies of the Hippoboscid and several other families were also included in the term *zevuv*. These insects were great pests, and their harm as dirt carriers was not always appreciated. They also can spread typhoid, anthrax, cholera, and a large number of other diseases. Where man and dirt combine, flies abound. Swarms of *Musca domestica* in the East corrupt and destroy anything edible which is not carefully covered from them, polluting a dish of food in a very few minutes. Just as so many of the inhabitants of Egypt, Palestine, and Arabia, still live much as their ancestors did 2 or 3 thousand years ago, so the flies continue to cause babies to die of dysentery just as they did in the days of Joshua, Herod, or Mohammed. Flies, however, are not all bad, for they also act as scavengers and sometimes as wound healers. The fly larvae act as wound healers because their digestive juices (principally urea) dissolve away dead and diseased tissue and do away with bacteria, acting as a powerful antiseptic. This was discovered only in World War I.

The Muscid flies are insects that undergo complete metamorphosis, with the female laying about 100 to 150 eggs at a time, and some are ovoviviparous, laying larvae. The larvae or maggots are often erroneously called "worms" by many. These feed on all manner of decaying animal and vegetable matter and thus actually do a great service in disposing of waste. Flies breed in practically all decaying and fermenting plant and animal wastes. As the adult is forming within the pupa, no provision is made for it to break out, except by a bladder, called a ptilinum. This bursts through a slit on the front of the insect's head and pulsates, being thrust in and out as the blood is pumped into it. This

* The males of the Order *Strepsiptera* or Twist-winged Flies have the front pair of wings reduced to little stubs, while the fore-wings of beetles form horny covers for the hind-wings when folded.

acts as a miniature battering ram, hitting the top of the puparium until it is pushed out and the adult creeps out. With this apparatus the fly works its way to the surface of the medium in which the larva pupated. In the open air the ptilinum withdraws and the slit in the head covers up. The blood is now forced into the wings, which stiffen, enabling the fly to take off in a few moments.

Flies are one of the most widely distributed insects on earth, possibly surpassed only by some arachnids. *Musca domestica* seems to have followed man all over the globe. Their powers of flight are well developed, making them capable of going great distances in search of food. Flies are so pertinacious that successful Egyptian generals were rewarded with golden collars bearing colossal silhouettes of the tiny animals—a wry tribute to their stubbornness in returning again and again to the same spot for food in spite of being shooed away. *Zevuv*, meaning obnoxious creatures, is a Hebrew name for some of these flies because they are so tormenting. The Phoenicians invoked the aid of their god Baal against the hordes of flies, and called him Baalzebub. The Jews in derision changed his name to Baalzebul, or "Master of the Dunghill."

77. Gnats

"*Ye* blind guides! which strain at a gnat, and swallow a camel" (Matt. 23:24).

Yav-chus is the Hebrew equivalent of the word "gnat," in the English version of the Bible. It is mentioned only in the New Testament. The word "gnat" is used in England somewhat ambiguously, and has a wide connotation. Originally it was synonymous with mosquitoes, but also included many other small, bloodsucking, two-winged flies. Today, it is customarily reserved for those that are *not* mosquitoes, and of both the Families *Culicidae* and *Chironomidae*. Several of these come in vast swarms at eventide, when they become troublesome. All these insects are distinguished by their long proboscis, which is a grooved sheath from which the insect shoots long, slender darts into the skin; the larvae and pupae always lie in water, emerging into the air only when they leave the chrysalis.

THE FLEAS (Order, *Siphonaptera*)

The Order *Siphonaptera* contains only the fleas. These are parasitic on other animals and notably warm-blooded ones; their mouth parts are formed into piercing and sucking tubes. The body is laterally compressed, the head is distinct but the thorax is composed of three hinged segments. The limbs progress in length, size, and strength backward and the animal can proceed by prodigious, for its size, leaps as well as by normal running and crawling. Fleas are all of very small size.

Fleas pass through a complete metamorphosis. The eggs are laid in the nests of the animals the adult parasitizes or in dust and trash, and the larvae, which are maggot-like, feed on debris, excrement, and any dried exudates found in the host's nest. There is a resting pupal stage. The adults are all parasites and usually one kind of flea is found on only one kind of host, but some can interchange, and they can live for considerable periods away from any host. The rat fleas are now well recognized as carriers of bubonic plague and other diseases lethal to man.

78. *Fleas*

The Common Flea, *Pulex irritans*, is found in all areas where unsanitary conditions abound, almost throughout the world. It is a great pest, with a painful bite that causes some swelling and itching. The natives of the area hate them, and the fleas can even "disturb Moslem equanimity." They may be one of the reasons why the Arabs change their camps so often.

The main danger from fleabites is the possible transmission of diseases, mainly the bubonic plague. *Bacillus pestis* or *Pasteurella pestis*, the cause of the plague, incubates in the flea's stomach, and from there is transmitted by the flea's bites. The fleas pick up this bacillus from animals, mainly the Black Rat, before the plague is passed on to man. Thus, control of the plague depends on the eradication of the rat population because this is the reservoir for the bacterium.

During the 1500 years before Christ, there were 41 recorded epidemics. There were 109 epidemics up to A.D. 1500, and 45 epidemics have been counted from 1500 to 1720. The first authenticated plague began in A.D. 542, in Pelusium, in Egypt, a trade center between East and West. By means of the trade routes, the disease spread until every country then known became afflicted, from China to Ireland. At its height, 5000 persons died daily, with the numbers sometimes going as high as 10,000. The author Procopius wrote: "It spared neither island nor cave nor mountain top where man dwelt . . . Many houses were left empty and it came to pass that many from want of relatives or servants lay unburied for several days. At that time it was hard to find anyone at business in Byzantium. Most people who met in the streets were bearing a corpse. All business had ceased. All craftsmen had deserted their crafts."

Only after 200 years did the epidemic subside. The second pandemic of plague, the Black Death, started in Mesopotamia about A.D. 1050 and reached its height in the fourteenth century, ending in the seventeenth century. The Crusaders, coming home from the Holy Land, may have helped spread this epidemic. During the course of the disease, one quarter of the world's population, about 25 million, died. In London, from 1664 to 1665, 70,000 people died out of a population of a half million. The last epidemic started in 1871, reaching its peak in 1907. Most of the seaports of the world felt its sting, even the United States, though modern measures prevented uncontrolled ravages.

There are about a thousand different known kinds of fleas. They are attracted by warmth. Both the males and the females are bloodsuckers, and under normal conditions blood is needed for pairing and oviposition. They have a long life span; some have lived for 18 months, and if the moisture and temperature are favorable the adults can live for a year or longer without food. They are such voracious feeders that they will often expel undigested blood from their intestines so they can take in more at the mouth.

These animals are flat from side to side, enabling them to move among hairs. They have strong, spine-like hairs projecting back from the posterior edges of their bodies so that as they climb up they will not slip back. Their feet are claw-like so they can hang onto hair. They have a great ability to jump, and starved female fleas have been seen to jump 11½ inches on a smooth wood surface. Perpendicularly, a jump of at least 7¾ inches has been measured.

The Lice (Order, *Anoplura*)

This Order of insects is divided into two suborders, those of the Bird- or Feather-Lice (*Mallophaga*), and the Sucking Lice (*Siphunculata*). The former bite instead of suck and are confined to birds; the latter parasitize mammals, even some aquatic ones like the seals. They occur on many kinds of mammals, including man, who is host to two distinct forms, the Head Louse (*Pediculus humanus*), and the Pubic or Crab Louse (*Phthirius pubis*). All lice are wingless, with bodies much flattened from back to underside; the limbs are armed with large, recurved claws so that the animals may cling firmly to the skin of their host. To this end also, the openings of their breathing apparatus have moved from the normal lateral position to their backs.

79. Lice

The *sciniphs* referred to in the Bible are lice, which were the third plague of Egypt. Since they are involved in the spread of typhus, this may be what was meant by the plague, though they make life uncomfortable enough by themselves. One louse found on man is *Pediculis humanus*, which can be found on the head (and given the subspecies name, *capitus*) or on the body (where it is *P. humanus corporis*). The two are very much alike. Body lice are seldom, if ever, found on the head, while head lice may be found on the body.

All lice are adapted to clinging to hairs by their claw-like feet, but body lice also find refuge in the clothing man uses. These create an intolerable itch when present in large numbers, and may be painful because they have piercing mouth parts. During the biting process the saliva injected into the wound prevents the host's blood from coagulating as it is sucked through the slim mouth parts. Lice seem never to be satisfied for long with one meal, but go on feeding all the time. Skin disorders can be caused by their bites. These animals are dangerous because they are carriers of diseases, especially typhus and cholera. In February, 1915, this disease killed 500 people a day in Serbia. Typhus is largely controlled by eradicating lice.

Lice also spread trench fever and relapsing fever, and so have probably played a more important part in the history of the world, and have had more to do with the winning of wars and battles, than all the generals and admirals put together. In past wars, diseases carried by lice accounted for more casualties among the soldiers than did all the assaults of their enemies.

On one occasion during World War I, approximately 10,000 lice and as many nits were found on a single army shirt, illustrating the numbers of these.

Robert Hooke wrote: "This is a creature so officious that 'twill be known to every one at one time or other, so busy, and so impudent, that it will be intruding itself in everyone's company, and so proud and aspiring that it fears not to trample on the best, and affects nothing so much as a crown; feeds and lives very high, and that makes it so saucy as to pull any one by the ears that comes its way, and will never be quiet till it has drawn blood."

A contemporary of St. Thomas à Becket wrote that on the morning after the saint's murder his robes were taken off, and the haircloth underwear was so infested with lice that they "boiled over" as the cloth was being taken off.

Human lice have eyes, while all the rest are blind. They vary in color according to the race of man they are found on. Lice multiply rapidly. The female can lay 50 eggs every week, which hatch every month. The size of the second generation would be about 2500. The third generation would be about 125,000.

THE GRASSHOPPERS AND LOCUSTS (Order, *Orthoptera*)

This is a large and very ancient order of insects that includes besides the grasshoppers, of which locusts are but a form, the crickets, the roaches, the mantises, and the stick- and leaf-insects. Their distribution is universal. The grasshoppers are divided into two great groups, the Short-horned (Family, *Locustidae*), and the Long-horned, together with the Cave Crickets (Family, *Tettigoniidae*). There are over 5,000 known species of the former; over 4,000 of the latter.

80. Locust

"Thou shalt carry much seed out into the field, and shalt gather *but* little in; for the locust shall consume it" (Deut. 28:38).

"If there be in the land famine, if there be pestilence, blasting, mildew, locust, *or* if there be caterpillar; if their enemy besiege them in the land of their cities; whatsoever plague, whatsoever sickness *there be;*" (I Kings 8:37).

"If there be dearth in the land, if there be pestilence, if there be blasting, or mildew, locusts, or caterpillers; if their enemies besiege them in the cities of their land; whatsoever sore or whatsoever sickness *there be:*" (II Chron. 6:28).

"He gave also their increase unto the caterpiller, and their labour unto the locust" (Ps. 78:46).

"There shall the fire devour thee; the sword shall cut thee off, it shall eat thee up like the cankerworm: make thyself many as the cankerworm, make thyself many as the locusts" (Nah. 3:15).

The Hebrews distinguished between the flying form (generation) of these insects, and the nonflying intermediate generation, but they seem to have used their word for the latter (*chor-gorv*) to cover also the other short-horned grasshoppers.

ARACHNIDS

The Spiders (Order, *Araneae*)

A deep waist separating the cephalothorax from the abdomen is one of the chief characteristics of the true spiders. In most species, the abdomen lacks segmentation and is covered by a soft, hairy integument, or a hard horny cuticle. The cephalothorax is covered by a carapace, in which are usually set eight eyes. The four pairs of walking legs are arranged radially around the cephalothorax. The large mandibles contain a poison gland which is connected to a pair of fangs. Characteristic of most spiders is the presence, on the underside of the abdomen, of a pair of spinnerets which connect with the silk glands, and from which the web is extruded.

81. Spider

"Whose hope shall be cut off, and whose trust *shall be* a spider's web" (Job 8:14).

"The spider taketh hold with her hands, and is in kings' palaces" (Prov. 30:28).

The Hebrew word *akkabish*, which signifies some kind of spider, occurs twice in the Bible: Isaiah 59:5 and Job 8:14. In both cases, reference is made to the frailty of spider webs by comparing them to the works of the wicked, which shall be so easily swept away. We cannot identify the type of spider from either passage, other than the fact that it is a web-spinner, many species of which are found in Palestine.

THE SCORPIONS (Order, *Scorpionida*)

The scorpions are characterized by an elongated body composed of 18 segments. The last 5 segments are narrowed abruptly to form a tail, at the end of which is located the telson, or poison sting.

82. *Scorpion*

The entire abdomen, including the tail, is distinctly segmented. The upper surface of the thorax, however, is covered by a single plate, bearing the eyes, which vary from 6 to 8 in number. The two foremost pairs of appendages are modified into nippers, the first pair forming small mandibles, the second pair, large pincers or chelae. The four pairs of walking legs are similar, and each is tipped with a pair of claws.

Scorpions (Hebrew *akrabiim*) are common throughout Palestine, being found in cracks and crevices of buildings as well as under rocks and brush in desert country. The venom of the scorpion is potent, and the sting of a large specimen can sicken a man for a considerable period of time. Death may even result if the victim is very young or in a weakened condition.

Biblical references to the scorpion allude either to its dangerous sting or to its habit of living in desolate places. "Who led thee through that great and terrible wilderness, *wherein were* fiery serpents, and scorpions, and drought; where *there was* no water; who brought thee forth water out of the rock of flint . . ." (Deut. 8:15). "And they had tails like unto scorpions, and there were stings in their tails: and their power *was* to hurt men five months" (Rev. 9:10).

MOLLUSCS (Phylum, *Mollusca*)

The *Mollusca* form one of the largest phyla with now almost 100,000 recorded species with a seeming infinity of variation of shell structure and color. Molluscs in the form of land snails range from the tops of mountains where there is vegetation, to the seashores, and sea snails extend from there to the ocean depths; they are found from the North Pole itself, under the ice on the ocean bottom, to the shores of Antarctica. Some snails can tolerate great aridity, being able to seal themselves into their shells and go into a state of suspended animation for years.

83. Snails (General)

The occasional Biblical references to molluscs (or shellfish) usually concern derivative products rather than the living animal. In Dan. 5:7, there is found the Hebrew word *argaman,* which signified the regal purple color so highly prized by the ancients: ". . . *And* the king spake, and said to the wise *men* of Babylon, Whosoever shall read this writing, and shew me the interpretation thereof, shall be clothed with scarlet [or, purple], and *have* a chain of gold about his neck, and shall be the third ruler in the kingdom." Because of its rarity and expense, purple became synonymous with royalty and power throughout the ancient world. In republican Rome, it was used to trim the togas of the consuls; during the more opulent days of the empire, the Caesars were fully clothed in the rich hue. Actually, the color in question was not a true purple, but more of a crimson. It was compared by the ancients to the color of newly clotted blood.

The costly dye from which this color was obtained was prepared from the bodies of two species of Mediterranean marine gasteropod mollusc or "snail," *Murex branderis* and *Murex trunculus.* The preparation very likely involved crushing the bodies of the molluscs to a pulpy mass into which fabric could be dipped, although the exact method was kept a closely guarded secret. The Phoenician city of Tyre was the center of the purple dye industry, and for this reason the color is often referred to as Tyrian purple. Archaeologists excavating the site of the ancient city have found large quantities of crushed *Murex* shells.

That the art of preparation was a well-kept secret is evident from the writings of the Talmudists, who seem to have had only vague ideas as to the source of the dye. They knew it was derived from a marine mollusc, but thought that the animal appeared only once in 70 years.

In Exod. 30:34–35, reference is made to "onycha," Hebrew *shecheleth,* as an important ingredient of incense: "And the Lord said unto Moses, Take unto thee sweet spices, stacte, and onycha, and galbanum; *these* sweet spices, with pure frankincense: of each shall there be a like *weight.* And thou shalt make it a perfume, a confection after the art of the apothecary, tempered together, pure *and* holy . . ."

Onycha is the horny, clawlike operculum of a Near Eastern member of the molluscan family *Strombidae.* This family enjoys a worldwide distribution, and is represented along our own shores by the familiar Queen Conch, *Strombus gigas,* of Florida. The operculum is used for offense, for defense, and, in some cases, as a unique means of locomotion. By extending its foot, embedding the sharp end of the operculum in the substratum, and then contracting, the animal is able to bump along quite rapidly. When burned, the opercula give off a sharp, strong scent, and, when mixed with more fragrant but less powerful substances, add greatly to their potency. The name "onycha" is derived from the Greek word "onyx," which signifies a nail or claw.

One of the few references to living snails occurs in Ps. 58:8: "As a snail *which* melteth, let *every one of them* pass away; *like* the untimely birth of a woman, *that* they may not see the sun" (Hebrew, *shablul*). This undoubtedly refers to a belief held by the ancients that the slimy track made by a snail as it crawled along was subtracted from the substance of its body, and that the farther it crawled, the smaller it became until it was entirely wasted away.

Land snails are a very numerous group in the Near East—as almost everywhere else for that matter. Certain fresh-water forms serve as hosts for the Schistosome worm or fluke parasites which cause the dread disease Bilharzia. There are literally hundreds of different species in the area, so that pinning the reference to any one species is both impractical and impossible, even if the Hebrew term ever had specific meanings.

THE SEGMENTED WORMS (Phylum, *Annelida*)

Another Phylum of considerable size and very great importance is represented in the Bible by one form. This is that of the *Annelida* which contains the earthworms, and a host of marine and some fresh-water forms including the leeches. The segmented worms, as they may be popularly and collectively called, are of the utmost importance to life on this planet as it is today, for, in the form of earthworms, they play a vital part in the formation of soil and thus of the whole of plant economy. And, all land animals including ourselves are dependent upon plants and plant growth. The Annelids of the sea also play a very important role in the general scheme of things but nothing compared to their terrestrial cousins. The freshwater forms are not of such great import but they fill some needed niches.

The Leeches (Class, *Hirudinea*)

The leeches comprise a small group of segmented worms that are mainly characterized by the presence of a posterior, and sometimes also an anterior, sucker. When present, the anterior sucker surrounds a mouth armed with three semicircular toothed jaws. The head is usually provided with five pairs of eyes, arranged along the first few segments. Although many leeches are external parasites, sucking the blood of fishes, amphibians, and mammals, others are active predators which seek out and devour earthworms, molluscs, and other small creatures.

84. Leech

In Prov. 30:15, we find the only occurrence in the Scriptures of the Hebrew word *alukah,* or "leech": "The horseleach hath two daughters, *crying,* Give, give. There are three *things that* are never satisfied, *yea,* four *things* say not, *It is* enough." That the translation of the word is correct is attested by the similarity of the Hebrew to the Arabic word for leech, *aluk.*

Leeches are common in the streams and rivers of the Near East. They often occur in such great numbers as to become annoying, if not dangerous, to the men and animals who attempt to utilize the streams for drinking and bathing. Most leeches can exist quite well on a diet of snails, insect larvae, crustaceans, and small worms, but given the opportunity they will voraciously drink blood from a vertebrate animal. The saliva of the bloodsucking leeches contains a powerful anticoagulant that not only prevents the formation of a clot, but helps preserve a blood meal for several months. A leech weighing a half ounce has been known to gorge itself with $2\frac{1}{2}$ ounces of concentrated blood, and then to exist for 15 months with no more to eat.

THE JELLYFISH AND CORALS (Phylum, *Coelenterata*)

The jellyfish, sea anemones, corals, and a considerable host of other marine and freshwater forms of soft-bodied animals are grouped together in the Phylum *Coelenterata.* Coral as we know it, is of course, a mineral growth or aggregation accumulated or formed by colonial animals which resemble tiny jellyfish all connected by a network of fine strands of tissue, and which may be called individually polyps. Coelenterates are of worldwide distribution in the sea, but the corals are confined to tropical and subtropical seas. Freshwater coelenterates also have a worldwide distribution between the polar circles wherever there is standing or running water, even ascending to considerable altitudes in mountain streams.

85. Coral

The ancients probably were not aware that coral is the remains of millions of microscopic animals, but they were very much aware of coral's beauty and prized it highly. Just as the American Indians prized certain rare seashells and used them for wampum, the Hebrews sought coral and used it as money along with precious stones, pearls, and gold. Even though the marine areas of the Middle East are particularly rich in fine coral formations, the Israelite market-places were not inundated by coral for gathering it was an extremely difficult task.

The Hebrew word for coral is *ramoth,* which means "that which grows high like a tree." This suggests that the Hebrews knew that coral, like pearls, but unlike gold or diamonds, grows—that is, it is something alive. But their exact knowledge of coral is questionable.

Coral is mentioned twice in the Old Testament, both times in conjunction with other precious objects. The Book of Job, so rich in natural history, uses coral to illustrate a homily: "No mention shall be made of coral, or of pearls: for the price of wisdom *is* above rubies" (Job 28:18).

The Book of Ezekiel lists coral among other commodities regularly traded by the ancients: ". . . they traded for thy wares with carbuncles, purple, and richly woven work, and fine linen, and coral, and rubies" (Ezek. 27:16).

It is interesting to note that, while coral is no longer a precious commodity, mostly because of modern under-water collecting techniques, it is still prized by many people for its splendid patterns and beautiful colors. It is not surprising at all that the Hebrews should have appreciated it so greatly.

THE SPONGES (Phylum, *Porifera*)

The lowliest group of multicelled animals is that of the sponges or *Porifera*. They are, in fact, on the borderline, for in some cases they are nothing more than colonies of bunches of single cells acting in concert, though differentiated. This is a fairly large Phylum and one whose members vary greatly in size, form, and habit. They are found in both salt and fresh water, but not on land. Many of them lay down internal skeletons to support their bulk, and different groups use different substances for this. Some accumulate calcium carbonate, the mineral forming chalk and limestone; others use silicon dioxide in a glassy form; still others make a horny substance which we all know, as it is the bathtub "sponge" of commerce. In life, the sponge of commerce looks like a slimy bun full of holes. These are channels through which water is circulated to bring minute particles of food to the colony. The range of shapes found within the Phylum includes such forms as cups, vases, tubes, spheres, and treelike branches, although many are shapeless. All are characterized by more or less complex internal canals that connect to the exterior by both large and small pores. Through these structures currents of nutrient-bearing water continually course through the animal. In order to support their bodies, sponges construct skeletons of calcium, silicon, or a chitinous material called "spongin." In some cases, combinations of the different substances are found. They are actually "colonial" entities, like some coelenterates such as the corals, being composed of a vast number of individual animals interconnected by strands of tissue.

86. Sponges

"And straightway one of them ran, and took a sponge, and filled *it* with vinegar, and put *it* on a reed, and gave him to drink" (Matt. 27:48).

"And one ran and filled a sponge full of vinegar, and put *it* on a reed, and gave him to drink, saying, Let alone; let us see whether Elias will come to take him down" (Mark 15:36).

"Now there was set a vessel full of vinegar: and they filled a spunge with vinegar, and put *it* upon hyssop, and put *it* to his mouth" (John 19:29).

The sponge is mentioned in the Bible only in connection with the Crucifixion of Jesus Christ. A Roman soldier dipped one in vinegar and held it to Jesus' lips. Considering the close proximity of all of Palestine to the Mediterranean Sea, it is probable that the ancient Hebrews were familiar with a variety of sponges.

Chapter 11
Dubious Animals of the Bible

"And it came to pass in the twelfth year, in the twelfth month, in the first *day* of the month, *that* the word of the Lord came unto me, saying, Son of man, take up a lamentation for Pharaoh king of Egypt, and say unto him, Thou art like a young lion of the nations, and thou *art* as a whale in the seas; and thou camest forth with thy rivers, and troubledst the waters with thy feet, and fouledst their rivers. Thus saith the Lord God, I will, therefore, spread out my net over thee with a company of many people; and they shall bring thee up in my net. Then will I leave thee upon the land, I will cast thee forth upon the open field, and will cause all the fowls of the heaven to remain upon thee, and I will fill the beasts of the whole earth with thee. And I will lay thy flesh upon the mountains, and fill the valleys with thy height. I will also water with thy blood the land wherein thou swimmest, *even* to the mountains; and the rivers shall be full of thee. And when I shall put thee out, I will cover the heaven, and make the stars thereof dark; I will cover the sun with a cloud, and the moon shall not give her light. All the bright lights of heaven will I make dark over thee, and set darkness upon thy land, saith the Lord God. I will also vex the hearts of many people, when I shall bring thy destruction among the nations, into the countries which thou hast not known" (Ezek. 32:1–9).

In this passage we have a skillful literary description of the coming misfortunes of Egypt. The imagery of the monster is rich and colorful and certainly succeeds in conveying the scenes of terror which the prophet intends. It is not certain what type of beast the Pharaoh is being compared to in the metaphor. Some interpret the monster as a crocodile. In this case, the picture of the animal "troubling" the waters with his feet is quite appropriate. The use of the image of turbidity to apply to Egypt's interference in the affairs of the Hebrews is an impressive literary device. It is difficult to infer the identity of the animal referred to in the passage. It appears to be a creature of unbelievable size. Furthermore, there is no certainty that the same animal is being mentioned throughout the comparison. This is not a literary deficiency on the part of Ezekiel, but indicative of a literary trait peculiar to ancient Near Eastern literature.

What were those monsters to which the Bible refers? Did they really exist, or were they merely the inventions of a primitive imagination? If they did exist in reality, are they represented by currently extant forms of animal life, or were they forms peculiar to their day and age, but now extinct?

It is also possible that we are here confronted with an extraordinary manner of describing ordinary animals. As our knowledge of ancient cultures increases, we are coming closer and closer to the solution. At any rate, we have passed the stage where the ancient myths are regarded as mere rhapsodies that contain no element of truth.

In the parable, Ezekiel predicts the plundering of Egypt by the Babylonians. Egypt valued the friendship of the small Palestinian states because they were situated between her and her rival empires of Assyria and Babylon. Numerous were the overtures she made to the Hebrews, promising them support and making every effort to arouse their antagonism against Assyria and Babylon. By failing to keep her promises, Egypt incurred the hostility of the Jews and the age-old appellation, "The Broken Reed." The images of filling the mountains with flesh and the water with blood may be a reference to the slain armies of the Pharaoh.

MANLIKE MONSTERS

There is speculation that a number of hominoid forms existed in Biblical times which today are extinct. Thus, in the first book of the Bible we find the phrase "There were giants (*nephilim*) in the earth in those days . . ." (Gen. 6:4). In the description of the Exodus there are references to the "Hairy Ones" (*Seirim*) who intimidated the Israelites during their wanderings in the desert. These were called by the alternate name *Sheidim* (the "destroyers"). The *Seirim* were about 4½ feet high, possessed long arms, and a great deal of red hair covering their bodies. They inhabited the area around the Sinai Peninsula, and were physiologically close enough to *Homo sapiens* to intermarry with them.

Manlike monsters are also popular mythological ingredients. Like Genesis, the Greek myths mention the existence of gigantic manlike creatures in the early days of creation. The mythologist Edith Hamilton describes them as: ". . . somewhat like men and yet unhuman. They had the shattering, overwhelming strength of earthquake and hurricane and volcano. In the tales about them they do not seem really alive, but rather to belong to a world where as yet there was no life, only tremendous movements of irresistible forces lifting up the mountains and scooping out the seas. The Greeks apparently had some such feeling because in their stories, although they represent these creatures as living beings, they make them unlike any form of life known to man."

Examples of these strange creatures are the Cyclopes and the Titans. There is another Greek legend which contains the postulation of successive experimental creations of man on the part of the gods. They started with a golden race of men, thence to a silver race, from there to a race of brass, etc.

The primary difficulty in determining the degree of truth in these myths is our inability to sympathize adequately with the minds of those who created and believed the myths. Perhaps the creatures that have been discussed here are purely fictitious; perhaps they were living remnants of very primitive peoples or even of *Homo erectus,* the precursor of *Homo sapiens,* as represented in fossil form by such as the Pithecanthropines and Australopithecines.

The Satyr

"But wild beasts of the desert shall lie there: and their houses shall be full of doleful creatures: and owls shall dwell there, and satyrs shall dance there" (Isa. 13:21).

"The wild beasts of the desert shall also meet with the wild beasts of the island, and the satyr shall cry to his fellow; the screech owl also shall rest there, and find for herself a place of rest" (Isa. 34:14).

The word "satyr," translated from the Hebrew *sa'ar,* is used only twice in the Bible. The Hebrew literally meant "shaggy or rough hair," and therefore is often translated as "wild goat." But to identify the satyr with a particular animal seems impossible, for the satyr in the Greek tradition was a mythological figure. Satyrs were purported to be demigods whose upper body was that of a man and whose lower half was the body of a goat.

Some scholars have thought that the satyr might have meant the wolf, since the Bible speaks of it as crying. This could refer to the eerie howling of the wolf, but just as well to the bleating of a goat. Both Tristram and Wood, Bible scholars of the nineteenth century, suggested that the satyr might be the dog-faced baboons that were worshiped in Egypt. But no one can really say whether the satyr was intended to refer to an animal or whether it applied only to some mythological figure.

The Dragon

"Their wine *is* the poison of dragons, and the cruel venom of asps" (Deut. 32:33).

"I am a brother to dragons, and a companion to owls" (Job 30:29).

"Thou shalt tread upon the lion and adder; the young lion and the dragon shalt thou trample under feet" (Ps. 91:13).

"And the wild beasts of the islands shall cry in their desolate houses, and dragons in *their* pleasant palaces: and her time *is* near to come, and her days shall not be prolonged" (Isa. 13:22).

"And Babylon shall become heaps, a dwellingplace for dragons, an astonishment, and an hissing without an inhabitant" (Jer. 51:37).

"Speak, and say, Thus saith the Lord God, Behold, I *am* against thee, Pharaoh king of Egypt, the great dragon that lieth in the midst of his rivers, which hath said, My river *is* mine own, and I have made *it* for myself" (Ezek. 29:3).

Practically every religion or mythology has its share of dragons. One of the more celebrated Sumerian myths tells of the slaying of the dragon *Kur,* and the ancient Greeks recorded the story of Hercules slaying the Hydra, a many-headed dragon which sprouted two new heads for every one cut off. Even Christianity has its dragon stories, notably the famous legend of St. George and the dragon. In most of these monster stories the dragon represents forces of evil which can be overcome only through the combined efforts of God and man.

Thus, Biblical references to the dragon can be regarded as symbolic—that is, the writer using the dragon in a fictional way. These references are a kind of shorthand evocation of the evil forces of the cosmos that are in conflict with man. When in Psalm 91 we find, "the young lion and the dragon shalt thou trample under feet," we can be almost certain the writer does not have in mind any conflict with a fire-breathing reptile, but rather that holiness shall triumph over evil when God's kingdom is established on earth.

The Hebrew word used to denote the dragon in these references is *tannin,* which means any great monster. Because the word is so vague it will have different connotations when it appears in various parts of the Bible. Sometimes it will have the symbolic meaning described above, while just as often it will signify some actual creature. Many Biblical scholars translate the word *tannin* as "jackal," denoting a mammal rather than a serpent. The related Hebrew word *than,* which means "dweller in a desolate place," is in the same way often translated as dragon, but it also probably refers to the jackal. When we read in Jeremiah: "And Babylon shall become heaps, a dwellingplace for dragons . . . ," we can probably assume that the writer means nothing more than that Babylon will be destroyed and made desolate, a dwelling place for jackals. Similarly, certain Biblical references to dragons may refer to crocodiles. For example, Ezekiel refers to "the great dragon that lieth in the midst of his rivers." This probably refers to the crocodiles that infest the banks of the Nile River. Another occurrence of the dragon is in Deuteronomy (32:33): "Their wine *is* the poison of dragons, and the cruel venom of asps." Here the writer can mean any one of a number of small poisonous serpents known to the ancient Hebrews.

A more unusual case is the reference in Nehemiah to a dragon well, apparently signifying a fountain located across the Jordan River from

Jerusalem. The Septuagint sheds some light on the usage here, indicating that a possible confusion of Hebrew words has taken place, and that a more accurate (and satisfactory) translation would be "fountain of the figs."

Not every mention of dragons in the Bible is so easily explained. In certain passages (Jer. 51:34, and others) the dragon mentioned is a specific monster that dwells in the ocean and is an adversary of God. Possibly the dragon here has a kinship to a monster named *Tiamet* which is a familiar figure in Babylonian and Assyrian mythology. The ancient Hebrews were quite naturally influenced by the religions around them, just as later they would influence the new religions of Christianity and Islam, and it is not too far-fetched to explain these dragons in this way. Furthermore, it would be highly unusual to attribute no belief in dragons to the Hebrews since almost every one of the ancient peoples had a considerable niche in their folklore reserved for giant reptiles.

The Sirrush

Generally in discussing dragons, one assumes that they did not exist and goes on to explain away references to them by the various methods already discussed. But what if dragons did exist? What if the writers of the Bible, who seem to have had an almost unbelievably accurate knowledge of zoology, mentioning animals found only in quite remote regions of the ancient world, had in mind an animal unknown to us but fitting the popular conception of what a dragon is? Such an assertion cannot be made flatly, but perhaps it is not as far-fetched as it seems.

In 1889, a German archaeologist working on the site of ancient Babylon brought to light the famed Ishtar Gate, an enormous brick arch built by the Babylonian ruler Nebuchadnezzar, covered with glazed bas-reliefs that showed various animals, including quite lifelike bulls, lions, and a creature that has come to be known as the Dragon of Babylon, also called the *sirrush*. The *sirrush* is at first sight a fantastic beast. The explicit bas-relief outline of it shows a serpent-like creature covered with scales. At the end of its long neck is a reptilian head from the nose of which arises a single sharp horn and from the mouth of which a forked tongue protrudes. Along the neck and at the back of the head are growths of skin that seem braided and adorned with knots. Most fantastic of all are the legs of the *sirrush;* the fore-legs resemble those of a feline animal, perhaps a panther with five small clawed fingers, while the hind-legs are shaped, taloned, and scaled like those of a bird. It has been shown that the *sirrush,* the Dragon of Babylon whose figure adorned the Ishtar Gate, is the same creature identified in the Bible by that name.

It may be that Nebuchadnezzar's artists used their imagination in drawing the dragon. But the juxtaposition of a purely mythical creature with easily recognizable lions and bulls does suggest to an open-minded observer the possibility that some creature resembling the *sirrush* did indeed exist at the time, and that it had been seen by at least some Babylonians and Hebrews. The creature, if it did exist, would be a throwback to the great age of dinosaurs that came to an end 78 million years ago. Is this impossible?

Scientists are still unsure exactly what conditions of climate and fauna led to the extinction of the dinosaurs. It is known that Africa was once well stocked with the big reptiles. Perhaps, in some remote jungle, conditions allowed a few "dragons" to survive. Scientists are constantly revising their judgments as new evidence—in all fields—is brought to light. Perhaps their statement that dinosaurs disappeared many millions of years before man appeared will prove to have exceptions. After all, the Crocodilians, the Chelonians, and the Tuatara, all older than the dinosaurs, survived.

Several unexplained phenomena strengthen the possibility that some strange creature named *sirrush* could have existed in Biblical times, indeed, might even live today. We are familiar with the many modern reports of sea serpents sighted by apparently reliable people, and never adequately explained away by mass hysteria, faulty eyesight, or the like. Similar reports often are recorded of people seeing various monsters inland. In particular, central Africa has been a rich source of such stories, coming not only from superstitious local people, but also from reliable, educated Europeans. Many of these reports suggest the existence of a creature similar in anatomy to the Ishtar Dragon. Now, central Africa is quite a long way from the site of ancient Babylon, but we need not assume that the animals portrayed on the Ishtar Gate were denizens of the Babylonian region.

Another creature, known Biblically as the *re'em*, but identified as a real animal called the Aurochs or Urus, was also displayed on the gate, and this also became totally extinct before modern science was established. Furthermore, it is now known that there was trade and direct contact between Mesopotamia and East Africa long before the time of Nebuchadnezzar. It seems likely that, if a *sirrush* had survived in central Africa, its proportions would have been known to the Babylonians. The Beast in the Pit might even have been a live specimen. There is, of course, no way of proving an assertion that the *sirrush* actually existed in Biblical times, but there is enough evidence to show that such an occurrence was not impossible.

But perhaps the most significant aspect of the *sirrush* conundrum is the fact that certain small dinosaurs exactly fitting the appearance of this beast are now known to have existed in the far past. These walked on their hind-legs and had legs and feet like birds; they had long serpentine tails; their bodies were covered with scales; their fore-limbs were short and they had "hands" with five fingers much like ours, or like those of a large cat with extended claws; and, most significant of all, they bore a single upright bone horn on their snouts. Being reptiles, they might well have had cloven serpentine tongues, and they could, like the iguanas of today, have borne crests down the backs of their necks. Dinosaurs were not all enormous; some were under 2 feet long. The animals described as being seen in Africa today are alleged to have bodies no bigger than donkeys and to be considerably less bulky than the largest living crocodiles in the over-all. Maybe one was brought to Babylon and kept in a pit such as those in which we keep large animals in our modern zoos.

The Unicorn

Even more tantalizing than the search for the *sirrush* is the ubiquitously legendary unicorn. The unicorn (the name means "one-horn") is best known for its appearance in Greek mythology, where it is described as a horse with a single horn protruding from its head. But the unicorn also appears in many places in the Bible, notably in the Book of Job and The Psalms. The original Biblical word for unicorn, however, has been shown to be none other than *re'em*, which, as we have seen, is a real animal, the extinct ox of western Eurasia. Why the *re'em* and the unicorn should have been confused is a simple matter. The Gate of Ishtar, following the artistic style of the place and period, showed its creatures in profile. Thus, the bi-horned *re'em*, in its appearance on the gate, appears to have but a single horn. Although that is probably the basis for the appearance of the unicorn in Biblical lore, the *re'em* quickly became mixed up with the Greek unicorn, and until modern times few people denied that unicorns actually existed.

The horn of the unicorn, known as the *alicorn*, was prized in the Middle Ages for its curative powers, and, as such a horn was very rare, it was literally worth its weight in gold. When one knows that the horn of the Indian rhinoceros is similarly prized in that country, the basis of the unicorn myth becomes more evident but still more confused. Many of the earliest descriptions of the unicorn tally closely with the Indian rhino, which, if we were not familiar with it, would be an unlikely enough beast. A well-known appearance of the unicorn comes in Talmudic lore surrounding the story of Noah's ark. That particular unicorn was said to have been so large that it could not fit in the ark, and was forced to swim behind it for the duration of the Flood, resting by supporting its alicorn on the boat.

The ultimate confusion in the story of the unicorn, both Biblical and Hellenistic, arose with the introduction into both the Near East and Europe of real alicorns—long, straight, and with a number of sinistrally twisted grooves. These were just as they are shown sticking out of the foreheads of the horselike beasts called unicorns.

They were, of course, the horns carried by a strange whale of the Arctic and sub-Arctic seas called the Narwhal (*Monodon monoceras*), and they reached the Mediterranean area from two directions: from the Greenland Norse settlements via Denmark, and from the coasts of eastern Siberia via the great trade routes across central Asia, that ended in Baghdad. It was from the combination of these Narwhal "horns" with the unicorns of the ancients that the medieval artists derived their standard unicorn of heraldry.

The Behemoth and the Leviathan

Almost as well known as the unicorn are the purely Biblical beasts, the behemoth and the leviathan, the former being a giant land animal, the latter a giant water beast. Like many other dubious Biblical creatures, the conceptions of these differ in their various appearances in the Scriptures. For example, we read in Isa. (27:1) that "In that day the Lord, with his sore, and great, and strong sword, shall punish leviathan the piercing serpent, even leviathan that crooked serpent; and he shall slay the dragon that *is* in the sea." The reference here is obviously to something quite different from the crocodile that the writer of Job has in mind when he says (41:1): "Canst thou draw out leviathan with an hook? or his tongue with a cord *which* thou lettest down?"

In general, however, the leviathan is a large *sea* monster, usually described as a fish, while the behemoth is a giant mammal, usually pictured in terms of a gigantic ox. Actually, the confusion stems from the root of each word. Behemoth is the plural form of a Hebrew word meaning "beast." As such it is used in the Bible to connote elephants, hippos, and other actual large land animals as well as its mythical counterpart. The word "leviathan" similarly stems from a Hebrew root word meaning "coil" or "twist," and thus is often used to signify some form of serpent in addition to the primary usage to indicate the king of the fishes.

There are several bizarre legends in Hebrew folklore concerning the leviathan and behemoth. For instance, it is said that there is but a single male and female of the species, and that the pair are not capable of producing baby behemoths, for a flourishing of these giants would overrun the world. Similarly, there are only two leviathans, which do not reproduce either, lest they crowd all other creatures from the ocean. It is said in apocryphal literature that on the Day of Judgment the righteous shall be permitted to view a colossal battle between leviathan and behemoth. First, the two beasts will be attacked by the angels, but they will repulse the heavenly host and begin a titanic encounter in which both will perish. The blessed will then be served a divine banquet of the flesh of these creatures. Often a giant bird called the *ziz* is added to form a triumvirate representing the three elements—earth, water, and air. The *ziz* is said to darken the sky with its wings, and once, when its egg was broken, the yolk and white flooded many cities.

The Cockatrice

While the behemoth and leviathan were noted for their hugeness, they never held sway over people's fears as did a small monster known as the cockatrice—or basilisk, as it is often called in the Bible. The cockatrice was the foul offspring of a cock's egg hatched by a venomous serpent. This creature is, of course, purely legendary. Some Bible scholars maintain that when the basilisk or *tzepha* (its Hebrew equivalent) was mentioned in the Bible, the writer had in mind nothing more than poisonous serpents in general, not something as bizarre as the cockatrice. Cocks simply do not lay eggs, and even if they did, no serpent would hatch the eggs, preferring instead to make of them a succulent repast.

Nevertheless, for many centuries the rumor of a cockatrice in the neighborhood terrified an ignorant populace, which not only believed that the animal existed, but that it was by far the most lethal creature in existence, killing plants and other animals with its very breath, sometimes even with a casual glance. According to legend, only the weasel was immune from the cockatrice's venom. The only way to kill a cockatrice, the legend insisted, was to hold a mirror up to it; its own image—the head of a cock upon the body of a serpent—would destroy it!

The belief in basilisks during the Middle Ages gave rise to a flourishing trade in "Jenny Hannivers," a commerce that still crops up now and again in isolated seacoast areas. A Jenny Hanniver is the body of a dead cockatrice. They were easy enough to obtain if your trade was fishing. Dead skates or rays, when properly shaped by means of a pocketknife, will easily take on the appearance of the legendary basilisk. As early as 1558, a writer recorded the purchase of a Jenny Hanniver, recognizing it for what it was. Others were more gullible, and the apothecary of the Middle Ages who did not have the body of a cockatrice hanging in his shop beside his alicorn was considered ill equipped. Why fake cockatrice bodies came to be called Jenny Hannivers is a mystery as impenetrable as the mystery of why people ever believed in the creatures in the first place.

The cockatrice was said to be deadly to those who felt its breath or met the glance of its eye. Most commentators seem sure that the Biblical verse refers to a viper of some kind. Tristram says that this is *Daboia xanthina*—i.e., a form of Russell's Viper—which he supposes was the fiery serpent mentioned by Moses.

The cockatrice was once held to be synonymous with the adder, but Biblical reference, if it refers to a snake at all, more likely indicates a puff adder (*Bitis*) or Daboia. The Daboia is actually a name for Russell's Viper (*Vipera russellii*) or the Tic-Polonga, a beautifully colored reptile about 5 feet long. It has a pale brown body with three longitudinal series of black rings enclosing spots of chocolate brown. This is the largest of the Asiatic vipers, but it is not found in the Holy Land. However, in northeast Asia Minor there is a large snake called the *Vipera xanthina*, which may be the snake referred to by Tristram in this connection.

Some puff adder would seem to fit the cockatrice best. These snakes are found throughout Africa and Asia and have remarkable ability to adapt to differing conditions. It is generally agreed that they are the "worst looking" of all the snakes; and they are as deadly as they look.

Puff adders are stout for their length, which is about 4 feet, and can be up to 9 inches in girth. Their fangs are enormously developed, and they inject their poison by a combination of a strike and a bite, as do the pit vipers. They mostly live in dry places, hiding in half-burnt grass or in sand. At night they come out to the trails of the small mammals on which they prey. They lie flat, with the forward part of the body in an S-shaped loop, ready to strike. They hiss violently with each inhalation and expulsion of breath, thus giving them the name "puff adder."

Puff adders are supposed to enter houses and farm buildings, where they hibernate during the cool months. Although their poison is effective, they are not really dangerous because of their slow, phlegmatic movements. There is a case where one hibernated in a woman's hat and other anecdotes are known which illustrate their supposed "friendliness."

There is one final explanation for the appearance of fabulous animals in the Bible, an explanation that is not really suitable for the creatures already discussed, but quite applicable to the assortment of mythical monsters described in the book of Revelation, an apocryphal book concerned mostly with the Judgment Day. The explanation is simply this: the writers of revelations and other mystical works either in the Bible or in the great body of related Biblical writings experienced "visions," or what we today would call hallucinations. While these hallucinations are rare today, they were quite common in earlier, more spiritual times, and led often to highly colorful and unusual descriptions of such things as hell and the Judgment Day. Thus, the book of Revelation talks about a beast that will appear on the Judgment Day with the head of a lion, the body of a horse, and the tail of a serpent. To complete the picture, the beast breathes fire and brimstone. Unlike, for example, the cockatrice, which was widely believed to exist, Revelation animals, like the above, are the personal expression of some form of religious mysticism.

Chapter 12

Plagues of the Bible

"Then the Lord said unto Moses, Go in unto Pharaoh, and tell him, Thus saith the Lord God of the Hebrews, Let my people go, that they may serve me" (Exod. 9:1).

Many of the events recorded in the Bible lie on the fringe of human understanding. Phenomena, or miracles, such as the ten plagues that befell Egypt and led to the Exodus of the Jewish people from that nation, would appear to be beyond modern man's experience. When we are told that the waters of the Nile turned to blood, or that the land was covered by darkness, we tend to dismiss these accounts as parable, allegory, or myth. This is because, to modern man, whether Jew, Christian, or Mohammedan—whether believer or disbeliever—these accounts seem to lack the preciseness we have come to expect from modern journalistic reports of almost equally strange happenings. Today, if we hear of many people dying somewhere, we know that some germ or virus is responsible. For the writers of the Bible, on the other hand, an equally explainable (from our point of view) event became a sign of divine intervention.

The plagues of Egypt, extraordinary as they seem, were all natural events. To say this does not necessarily deny the possibility of supernatural instigation of the plagues. It means that they are explainable in scientific as well as religious terms. Scientists today are ready to accept statements made in the Bible as straight fact. They have no reason to believe that the plagues, extraordinary though they seem, could not have occurred in Egypt at that time. No single one of the plagues is at all impossible or even extraordinary. It is the occurrence of *ten* natural disasters in one land at one time that strains belief. But unlikeliness doesn't mean impossibility.

The ten plagues were as follows:

1. The waters of the Nile were turned to blood. (Perhaps red clay was carried down from the upper Nile basin, giving the water a bloodlike appearance.)
2. There was a plague of frogs.
3. Innumerable lice appeared.
4. There came a plague of flies.
5. All domestic animals except those of the Hebrews died.
6. Men and animals broke out with boils.

7. There was a series of hailstorms.
8. Swarms of locusts appeared.
9. Darkness (perhaps dust storms) covered the land.
10. The "first born" of the Egyptians were smitten.

Five of the ten (2, 3, 4, 5, and 8) involve animals. Three others (5, 6, and 10) are, in some way or other, medical affairs, most likely attributable to some disease or virus. The darkness and the hailstorms are easily understandable natural events. To understand their vast significance, let us examine the background of the plagues.

The Hebrews sojourned in Egypt for a considerable time, in bondage but probably not as slaves *per se*. Their status seems to have been that of a second-class citizenry such as Hitler endeavored to impose upon the Jews of his short-lived "empire." But they were there for many generations, and undoubtedly came to know the wildlife of that country intimately. Therefore, we must inspect the Book of Exodus and especially the account of the plagues from a point of view other than that which we should adopt toward the later chapters of the Bible. Before and up to Exodus we are facing one thing, with its own history and philosophy; after Exodus, we confront several other complete ethos starting with that of the Hebrews as a nation and ending, if you are a Christian, with something altogether different. The comparatively brief period of the history of the Hebrews recorded in Exodus represents an intermediate and transitional stage in their history, alien to them but of enormous interest to us.

During the period of bondage in Egypt, the nomadic, pastoral Hebrew tribe lived in an ancient, settled, agricultural land inhabited by two distinct peoples—the indigenous fellahin who still live there, and the ruling, so-called Dynastic Egyptians, a lordly and intelligent people who had come into the country some 3000 years before. The latter ruled the former, come wars, revolutions, and all other disasters, for 4000 years; religious precept wielded by an all-pervading priestly hierarchy secured their power. From time to time these ruling Egyptians conquered other peoples, but they never remained in control of them. They always withdrew into their delta and river channel to brood and resuscitate their ancient religious motives. People invaded them too—the mysterious Hyksos, the Assyrians, the Persians, and the Greeks—but they, too, all finally withdrew, while Ancient Egypt continued, sullied but for the most part unchanged.

These Dynastic Egyptians enslaved many peoples, mostly desert tribes from neighboring territories in Libya and the Red Sea coast, but these people were just absorbed into the underlying mass of the fellahin. Nubians were brought in, in great numbers, but they simply vanished.

The Hebrews alone remained in this autocratic realm as a unit *and multiplied there*. This was really extraordinary and was a constant source of irritation to the current ruling dynasty. The cry was, "Why won't the Hebrews integrate?" Why, the Pharaohs asked, would not this stubborn breed give up their strange God, do obeisance to Ra, admit the omnipotence of Amen, and join the rest of the fellahin? It puzzled the priests as well as the lay rulers. For hundreds of years both tried to lash, push, persuade, and cajole the Hebrews into at least religious cooperation. Everything they tried failed, for the Hebrews had their very personal God and, to the last female child, not only believed in His omnipotence, but in His infallibility as well. They had no need of Ra, or even of Amen, the universal spirit.

By 1200 B.C., Egypt was in turmoil. The situation between the Egyptian rulers and the Hebrew people became intolerable to both. The Hebrews had by that time acquired a very real importance. As a well-integrated and stable community, they could speak to the Pharaoh, face to face, and on an equal footing—and they did so, with their leader, Moses, as their spokesman.

Moses was not only the elected chieftain of a vast tribe; he was an exceptional man, a born leader, and a practical mystic. The Pharaoh was no match for him. Moses had been brought up and educated by the ruling aristocracy, and so knew all their tricks. As the leader of his people, he knew full well that the time to leave had come—that it was now or never.

Moses was a very learned and wise man and he had had access to the thousands of years of accumulated knowledge of the plodding priests of the land—a land controlled wholly and annually by the activities of the mighty Nile River. Moses obviously picked his time as well as his Pharaoh. Then he struck. And he brought to bear upon his righteous task every possible ethical, moral, religious, traditional, atavistic, practical—even mystical—force he could muster. He even employed psychology of a most advanced and, in some respects, modern order. And he was inspired by, and filled with, the power of his God.

So Moses achieved the deliverance of the Hebrew people from the land of Egypt. He did this, the Bible tells us, by demonstrating the power of his God to the Egyptian rulers in the form of the plagues which tormented the Egyptians for about a year. The Bible makes clear, however, that all of the plagues were natural phenomena, familiar to the people of Egypt, but unusual on this occasion by their intensity, their violence, and their close sequence. Thus, the power of the Hebrew Deity is shown in the Bible by the subjugation of natural forces to His Will.

Now, we can take this in several ways. First, we can believe that the plagues were wholly natural and that Moses used their occurrence psychologically to frighten the Egyptians into granting his request. Or, we can believe that some mysterious teleological relationship between natural and supernatural forces was being demonstrated. Or, going even farther, we can believe that Moses, extraordinary man that he was, whether through some remarkable (but perfectly reasonable) control over the elements or through some form of mass suggestion, in some way was able to bring about a belief on the part of both Hebrews and Egyptians that his God was causing these events. In any case, there seems little reason to doubt that the events as recorded in the Bible *did* take place.

Exodus attempts to emphasize the Divine interest in human affairs: God's provident care over an enslaved people and His subsequent punishment of their oppressors. The virtues toward which the book especially points are justice, mercy, and righteousness. We cannot help but recognize the immanent quality of the Hebrew God, His indescribable proximity to man and His mysterious participation in all of his triumphs and setbacks.

The power of God is expressed, in the Book of Exodus, through these events which achieved the deliverance of the Hebrews and made known God's power in Egypt and throughout the world. The revelation of God, as subjecting the forces of Nature to *His Will*, demonstrates the mysterious teleological relationship between the natural and the supernatural order, as understood by these remarkable people—the Hebrews.

Subsequent to the initial "plague," which was but an exceptional flood bearing silt of a dark reddish hue, the plagues went as follows:

PLAGUE NO. 2—FROGS

"And the Lord spake unto Moses, Go unto Pharaoh, and say unto him, Thus saith the Lord, Let my people go, that they may serve me. And if thou refuse to let *them* go, behold, I will smite all thy borders with frogs: And the river shall bring forth frogs abundantly, which shall go up and come into thine house, and into thy bedchamber, and upon thy bed, and into the house of thy servants, and upon thy people, and into thine ovens, and into thy kneadingtroughs; And the frogs shall come up, both on thee, and upon thy people, and upon all thy servants. And the Lord spake unto Moses, Say unto Aaron, Stretch forth thine hand with thy rod over the streams, over the rivers, and over the ponds, and cause frogs to come up upon the land of Egypt. And Aaron stretched out his hand over the waters of Egypt; and the frogs came up, and covered the land of Egypt. And the magicians did so with their enchantments, and brought up frogs upon the land of Egypt. Then

Pharaoh called for Moses and Aaron, and said, Entreat the Lord, that he may take away the frogs from me, and from my people; and I will let the people go, that they may do sacrifice unto the Lord. And Moses said unto Pharaoh, Glory over me: when shall I entreat for thee, and for thy servants, and for thy people to destroy the frogs from thee and thy houses, *that* they may remain in the river only? And he said, To morrow. And he said, *Be it* according to thy word; that thou mayest know that *there is* none like unto the Lord our God. And the frogs shall depart from thee, and from thy houses, and from thy servants, and from thy people; they shall remain in the river only. And Moses and Aaron went out from Pharaoh: and Moses cried unto the Lord because of the frogs which he had brought against Pharaoh. And the Lord did according to the word of Moses; and the frogs died out of the houses, out of the villages, and out of the fields. And they gathered them together upon heaps; and the land stank" (Exod. 8:1–14).

The frogs of Egypt, like frogs elsewhere and even in the tropical rain forests, have a single breeding season, and this is dependent on the sidereal year. However, it is affected by both temperature and humidity —the latter in the form of surface water from rainfall or melting snow and ice. In regions of equable climate such as tropical rain forests or temperate regions of high rainfall, the annual breeding date may be extraordinarily precise. Long-term research in western Europe has shown that the common frog *Rana temporaria* invariably consummates each phase of its breeding, metamorphosis, and migration on the first day after a certain date when the temperature first reaches and maintains a specific point. The frogs of the Nile are faced with quite different seasonal problems.

The river flows through a desert in Egypt and Nubia (the Sudan), and there is virtually no rainfall at all except in the extreme north on the delta where the seasons are like ours of the northern temperate belt. Thus, the frogs of the Nile valley proper breed when the floods come, and these floods move slowly downstream, northward, starting at Khartoum in August and September while the maximum at Cairo is in October.

In case of an exceptional flood, or one at a time of year other than the normal, the frogs may be thrown out of "gear," as not infrequently happens in the tropics, and a veritable "plague" might then occur. That this happened on the occasion of the exceptional flood described in Exodus hardly needs to be questioned. And this would, indeed, be a plague, for, on the sudden retreat of a flood that has started frogs breeding over a wide area, millions of the animals are left high and dry to die, to stink in the hot son, and to attract flies.

PLAGUE NO. 3—LICE

"But when Pharaoh saw that there was respite, he hardened his heart, and hearkened not unto them; as the Lord had said. And the Lord said unto Moses, Say unto Aaron, Stretch out thy rod, and smite the dust of the land, that it may become lice throughout all the land of Egypt. And they did so: for Aaron stretched out his hand with his rod, and smote the dust of the earth, and it became lice in man and in beast; all the dust of the land became lice throughout all the land of Egypt. And the magicians did so with their enchantments to bring forth lice, but they could not: so there were lice upon man, and upon beast. Then the magicians said unto Pharaoh, This *is* the finger of God: and Pharaoh's heart was hardened, and he hearkened not unto them; as the Lord had said. And the Lord said unto Moses, Rise up early in the morning, and stand before Pharaoh; lo, he cometh forth to the water; and say unto him, Thus saith the Lord, Let my people go, that they may serve me" (Exod. 8:15–20).

There are a number of different interpretations of the word "lice" in the preceding verses. Some take it to mean lice, while others claim that it refers to mosquitoes.

Mosquitoes belong to a different class of insects from that of the lice. Actually, the colloquial term "lice" includes two families of insects: the *Siphunculata* which, as was explained above, live on mammals, and the *Mallophaga*, which live on birds. Lice are bloodsuckers and are transmitted to new host individuals through bodily contact. They can spend their entire life cycle on the same host.

The mosquitoes thrive in hot and damp climates, rendering sleep impossible. The common Egyptian mosquito (*Culex pipiens*) is small, ash-colored, and has white spots on its legs. The ancient Egyptians were known to have used mosquito nets in an effort to minimize this discomfort. Female mosquitoes feed mostly on blood of animals, which causes them to inflict painful bites on man and beast. The correlation between the changes in the Nile and the proliferation of frogs and "lice"—if mosquitoes were meant—reveals the writer of Exodus to be accurate from a scientific standpoint. The reference to the dust of the land becoming lice contains some interesting implications. Even if we interpret it as a literary device, it is a mechanism well engineered. It may also imply, however, a belief on the part of the Hebrews in the spontaneous generation of animate from inanimate matter. The belief in spontaneous generation was widespread throughout the world and persisted through the centuries until Louis Pasteur refuted it in the middle of the nineteenth century. It was commonly applied to larval animals. This mention would, however, seem to indicate lice being lice rather than mosquitoes which were well known to be associated with marshes and water. Sudden increased humidity does, moreover, foster the breeding of body lice.

PLAGUE NO. 4—FLIES

"Else, if thou wilt not let my people go, behold, I will send swarms *of flies* upon thee, and upon thy servants, and upon thy people, and into thy houses; and the houses of the Egyptians shall be full of swarms *of flies*, and also the ground whereon they *are*. And I will sever in that day the land of Goshen, in which my people dwell, that no swarms *of flies* shall be there; to the end thou mayest know that I *am* the Lord in the midst of the earth. And I will put a division between my people and thy people: to morrow shall this sign be. And the Lord did so: and there came a grievous swarm *of flies* into the house of Pharaoh, and *into* his servants' houses, and into all the land of Egypt; the land was corrupted by reason of the swarm *of flies*. And Pharaoh called for Moses and for Aaron, and said, Go ye, sacrifice to your God in the land. And Moses said, It is not meet so to do; for we shall sacrifice the abomination of the Egyptians to the Lord our God: lo, shall we sacrifice the abomination of the Egyptians before their eyes, and will they not stone us? We will go three days' journey into the wilderness, and sacrifice to the Lord our God, as he shall command us. And Pharaoh said, I will let you go, that ye may sacrifice to the Lord your God in the wilderness; only ye shall not go very far away; entreat for me. And Moses said, Behold, I go out from thee, and I will entreat the Lord that the swarms *of flies* may depart from Pharaoh, from his servants, and from his people, to morrow: but let not Pharaoh deal deceitfully any more in not letting the people go to sacrifice to the Lord. And Moses went out from Pharaoh, and entreated the Lord. And the Lord did according to the word of Moses; and he removed the swarms *of flies* from Pharaoh, from his servants, and from his people: there remained not one. And Pharaoh hardened his heart at this time also, neither would he let the people go" (Exod. 8:21–32).

There are a number of possible interpretations of the plague of flies. One opinion claims that it is identical with the preceding plague. Therefore, we have one story drawn from two different sources. Others choose to endow the plague with more individuality. The Hebrew word used to describe the animals is *arob*, which implies a mixture; i.e., "all sorts of flies." In Psalm 78, this same word is used, describing the creature as devouring the Egyptians.

In this case some "scholars" have suggested that a likely candidate is *Blatta aegyptica*, the Egyptian cockroach. The Egyptian cockroaches are as great a nuisance as mosquitoes. They eat everything in sight and they are capable of inflicting severe bites on man. For this reason they became objects of appeasement, occupying a considerable place among Egyptian sacred creatures. They are found frequently in Egyptian sculpture and painting. They are the same size as our common cockroach (*Blatta orientalis*), black in color with a white band on an oval corselet.

However, since the Bible says "flies," and even uses a recognized Hebrew word that denotes "all kinds of flies"—and since the writers of the Bible were manifestly such excellent zoologists—is it not much more reasonable to accept their statement at face value in this case? Further, as was pointed out above, flies are the natural aftermath of floods even if excessive numbers of dead animals are not left by the retreating waters. Among such flies are, in addition to the common House Fly (*Musca domestica*), the even more troublesome bluebottles, the greenbottles, the warbleflies and the botflies. The last named, moreover, take longer to swarm and among them are the loathsome *ver macaques*, beefworm flies, and screwworm flies that lay their eggs in the skins of men and beasts. These afflictions were, be it noted, alluded to as "murrain" in livestock by the English about the time the Bible was translated.

PLAGUE NO. 5—MURRAIN UPON DOMESTIC ANIMALS

"Then the Lord said unto Moses, Go in unto Pharaoh, and tell him, Thus saith the Lord God of the Hebrews, Let my people go, that they may serve me. For if thou refuse to let *them* go, and wilt hold them still, Behold, the hand of the Lord is upon thy cattle which *is* in the field, upon the horses, upon the asses, upon the camels, upon the oxen, and upon the sheep: *there shall be* a very grievous murrain. And the Lord shall sever between the cattle of Israel, and the cattle of Egypt: and there shall nothing die of all *that is* the children's of Israel. And the Lord appointed a set time, saying, To morrow the Lord shall do this thing in the land. And the Lord did that thing on the morrow, and all the cattle of Egypt died: but of the cattle of the children of Israel died not one. And Pharaoh sent, and, behold, there was not one of the cattle of the Israelites dead. And the heart of Pharaoh was hardened, and he did not let the people go" (Exod. 9:1–7).

PLAGUE NO. 6—BOILS

"And the Lord said unto Moses and unto Aaron, Take to you handfuls of ashes of the furnace, and let Moses sprinkle it toward the heaven in the sight of Pharaoh. And it shall become small dust in all the land of Egypt, and shall be a boil breaking forth *with* blains upon man, and upon beast, throughout all the land of Egypt. And they took ashes of the furnace, and stood before Pharaoh; and Moses sprinkled it up toward heaven; and it became a boil breaking forth *with* blains upon man, and upon beast. And the magicians could not stand before Moses because of the boils; for the boil was upon the magicians, and upon all the Egyptians. And the Lord hardened the heart of Pharaoh, and he hearkened not unto them; as the Lord had spoken unto Moses. And the Lord said unto Moses, Rise up early in the morning, and stand before Pharaoh, and say unto him, Thus saith the Lord God of the Hebrews, Let my people go, that they may serve me. For I will at this time send all my plagues upon thine heart, and upon thy servants, and upon thy people; that thou mayest know that *there is* none like me in all the earth" (Exod. 9:8–14).

It is quite possible that the two plagues (murrain and boils) are identical except for the fact that the second one is applied to man. "Blains," to the sixteenth-century Englishman, meant painful blisters or pustules, but the nature of the disease involved in Egypt is unknown to us. It is just possible that it was the bubonic plague. It is unfortunate that there is no mention of a proliferation of rats to confirm this hypothesis, as there is in the plague of emerods on the Philistines. Another hypothesis is that it was smallpox. Like the plague, smallpox is both contagious and infectious, and like the plague, it is accompanied by considerable fever and chills. It is also accompanied by eruptions which often leave permanent scars on the victim. The smallpox virus is known to have serious effects upon cattle. In this form, the disease is referred to as cowpox. However, the most likely interpretation is, again, just what the Bible says—namely, murrain, or boils induced by fly eggs laid in the skins of men and animals.

PLAGUE NO. 7—HAIL

"As yet exaltest thou thyself against my people, that thou wilt not let them go? Behold, to morrow about this time, I will cause it to rain a very grievous hail, such as hath not been in Egypt since the foundation thereof even until now. Send therefore now, *and* gather thy cattle, and all that thou hast in the field; *for upon* every man and beast which shall be found in the field, and shall not be brought home, the hail shall come down upon them, and they shall die. He that feared the word of the Lord, among the servants of Pharaoh, made his servants and his cattle flee into the houses: And he that regarded not the word of the Lord left his servants and his cattle in the field. And the Lord said unto Moses, Stretch forth thine hand toward heaven, that there may be hail in all the land of Egypt, upon man, and upon beast, and upon every herb of the field, throughout the land of Egypt. And Moses stretched forth his rod toward heaven; and the Lord sent thunder and hail, and the fire ran along upon the ground: and the Lord rained hail upon the land of Egypt. So there was hail, and fire mingled with the hail, very grievous, such as there was none like it in all the land of Egypt since it became a nation. And the hail smote throughout all the land of Egypt all that *was* in the field, both man and beast; and the hail smote every herb of the field. Only in the land of Goshen, where the children of Israel *were*, was there no hail. And Pharaoh sent, and called for Moses and Aaron, and said unto them, I have sinned this time: the Lord *is* righteous, and I and my people *are* wicked. Entreat the Lord (for *it is* enough) that there be no *more* mighty thunderings and hail; and I will let you go, and ye shall stay no longer. And Moses said unto him, As soon as I am gone out of the city, I will spread abroad my hands unto the Lord; *and* the thunder shall cease, neither shall there be any more hail; that thou mayest know how that the earth *is* the Lord's" (Exod. 9:17–29).

From the passage above it is easy to conclude that this was a very painful plague. Hail results when there are considerable differences of temperature between the lower and higher levels of air. The presence of the colder layer causes the surrounding moisture to condense so suddenly that small "stones" of ice are formed. There are two kinds of hail: one kind consists of the tiny grains which precede a snowfall; the other is composed of hailstones. The latter occurs commonly in spring and summer, and quite frequently in tropical climates. The formation of the stones results from the contact of clouds of widely different temperatures. They consist of concentric layers, like an onion, with a nucleus of snow or ice. The usual range of their weight is from a few grains to several ounces, though at times they may reach half a pound. They commonly measure about one fourth of an inch in diameter. In hot climates, however, they are much larger, ranging from 2 to 5 inches in diameter.

Hailstorms are not frequent in Egypt. When they do occur, it is usually in January. In all likelihood the month in which this plague occurred was February. This assumption is borne out by the agricultural description, ". . . for the barley *was* in the ear, and the flax *was* bolled. But the wheat and the rie were not smitten; for they *were* not grown up" (Exod. 9:31–32). The "fire mingled with the hail" is a reference to lightning, a usual accompaniment of a hailstorm.

PLAGUE NO. 8–LOCUSTS

"And the Lord said unto Moses, Go in unto Pharaoh: for I have hardened his heart, and the heart of his servants, that I might shew these my signs before him: And that thou mayest tell in the ears of thy son, and of thy son's son, what things I have wrought in Egypt, and my signs which I have done among them; that ye may know how that

I *am* the Lord. And Moses and Aaron came in unto Pharaoh, and said unto him, Thus saith the Lord God of the Hebrews, How long wilt thou refuse to humble thyself before me? let my people go, that they may serve me. Else, if thou refuse to let my people go, behold, to morrow will I bring the locusts into thy coast: And they shall cover the face of the earth, that one cannot be able to see the earth: and they shall eat the residue of that which is escaped, which remaineth unto you from the hail, and shall eat every tree which groweth for you out of the field: And they shall fill thy houses, and the houses of all thy servants, and the houses of all the Egyptians; which neither thy fathers, nor thy fathers' fathers have seen, since the day that they were upon the earth unto this day. And he turned himself, and went out from Pharaoh. And Pharaoh's servants said unto him, How long shall this man be a snare unto us? let the men go, that they may serve the Lord their God: knowest thou not yet that Egypt is destroyed? And Moses and Aaron were brought again unto Pharaoh: and he said unto them, Go, serve the Lord your God: *but* who *are* they that shall go? And Moses said, We will go with our young and with our old, with our sons and with our daughters, with our flocks and with our herds will we go: for we *must hold* a feast unto the Lord. And he said unto them, Let the Lord be so with you, as I will let you go, and your little ones: look *to it;* for evil *is* before you. Not so: go now ye *that are* men, and serve the Lord; for that ye did desire. And they were driven out from Pharaoh's presence. And the Lord said into Moses, Stretch out thine hand over the land of Egypt for the locusts, that they may come up upon the land of Egypt, and eat every herb of the land, *even* all that the hail hath left. And Moses stretched forth his rod over the land of Egypt, and the Lord brought an east wind upon the land all that day, and all *that* night; *and* when it was morning, the east wind brought the locusts. And the locusts went up over all the land of Egypt, and rested in all the coasts of Egypt: very grievous *were they;* before them there were no such locusts as they, neither after them shall be such. For they covered the face of the whole earth, so that the land was darkened; and they did eat every herb of the land, and all the fruit of the trees which the hail had left: and there remained not any green thing in the trees, or in the herbs of the field, through all the land of Egypt. Then Pharaoh called for Moses and Aaron in haste; and he said, I have sinned against the Lord your God, and against you. Now, therefore, forgive, I pray thee, my sin only this once, and entreat the Lord your God, that he may take away from me this death only. And he went out from Pharaoh, and entreated the Lord. And the Lord turned a mighty strong west wind, which took away the locusts, and cast them into the Red sea; there remained not one locust in all the coasts of Egypt. But the Lord hardened

Pharaoh's heart, so that he would not let the children of Israel go" (Exod. 10:1-20).

In Asia Minor, Egypt, southern Asia, and Africa, locusts occur periodically in vast swarms. They bring famine and desolation to flourishing regions by devouring all the vegetation in sight. They are also a source of pestilence because of the putrefaction of their accumulated bodies. The description in Exodus of the abominable creatures covering "the face of the earth" is not just a literary device. In some parts of Africa they are known to cover the whole surface of the ground over areas of more than 2000 square miles. As though all this were not enough, they are known to poison the air with the fetid exhalation of their excrement, which can be smelled up to 150 miles away. They fly in compact formations large enough to blot out the light of the sun. As the Bible indicates, the course of their travels is very much affected by the wind. It is possible for a strong enough wind to destroy them. By the law of Moses, locusts were permitted as food. In some parts of Asia and Africa even today, they are commonly eaten, either broiled, stewed, or fried in butter.

PLAGUE NO. 9—DARKNESS

"But the Lord hardened Pharaoh's heart, so that he would not let the children of Israel go. And the Lord said unto Moses, Stretch out thine hand toward heaven, that there may be darkness over the land of Egypt, even darkness *which* may be felt. And Moses stretched forth his hand toward heaven; and there was a thick darkness in all the land of Egypt three days: They saw not one another, neither rose any from his place for three days: but all the children of Israel had light in their dwellings. And Pharaoh called unto Moses, and said, Go ye, serve the Lord; only let your flocks and your herds be stayed: let your little ones also go with you. And Moses said, Thou must give us also sacrifices and burnt offerings, that we may sacrifice unto the Lord our God. Our cattle also shall go with us; there shall not an hoof be left behind: for thereof must we take to serve the Lord our God; and we know not with what we must serve the Lord, until we come thither. But the Lord hardened Pharaoh's heart, and he would not let them go" (Exod. 10:20-27).

The darkness referred to above was probably caused by a sandstorm, a frequent occurrence in early spring in climates such as Egypt's. Some of the phrases above verify this assumption. Thus, the darkness is described as one "which may be felt." What else but a sandstorm could keep an entire people confined in their homes for three days? A sandstorm is ushered in by a hot wind from the desert which will last for two or three days at a time. The quantity of "sand"—actually very fine dust—in the air is so great as to darken the skies. The wind usually travels in a narrow zone, leaving the air clear on either side of the sand-storm.

PLAGUE NO. 10—DEATH OF THE FIRSTBORN

"And the Lord said unto Moses, Yet will I bring one plague *more* upon Pharaoh, and upon Egypt; afterwards he will let you go hence: when he shall let *you* go, he shall surely thrust you out hence altogether. Speak now in the ears of the people, and let every man borrow of his neighbour, and every woman of her neighbour, jewels of silver, and jewels of gold. And the Lord gave the people favour in the sight of the Egyptians. Moreover, the man Moses *was* very great in the land of Egypt, in the sight of Pharaoh's servants, and in the sight of the people. And Moses said, Thus saith the Lord, About midnight will I go out into the midst of Egypt: And all the firstborn in the land of Egypt shall die, from the firstborn of Pharaoh that sitteth upon his throne, even unto the firstborn of the maidservant that *is* behind the mill; and all the firstborn of beasts. And there shall be a great cry throughout all the land of Egypt, such as there was none like it, nor shall be like it any more. But against any of the children of Israel shall not a dog move his tongue, against man or beast; that ye may know how that the Lord doth put a difference between the Egyptians and Israel. And all these thy servants shall come down unto me, and bow down themselves unto me, saying, Get thee out, and all the people that follow thee: and after that I will go out. And he went out from Pharaoh in a great anger" (Exod. 11:1–8).

"And it came to pass, that at midnight the Lord smote all the firstborn in the land of Egypt, from the firstborn of Pharaoh that sat on his throne, unto the firstborn of the captive that *was* in the dungeon; and all the firstborn of cattle. And Pharaoh rose up in the night, he, and all his servants, and all the Egyptians; and there was a great cry in Egypt; for *there was* not a house where *there was* not one dead" (Exod. 12:29–30).

This is unquestionably the most terrible of all the plagues. People are slain no longer through the agency of disease or climatic conditions but directly by the hand of God. In addition, the firstborn are the ones who are killed. In ancient Near Eastern cultures, the position of the firstborn in a family was one of singular dignity. Thus, the Egyptians were confronted with the Hebrew God in all His power and wrath. It seems unfortunate that all the people of Egypt had to suffer in such a manner for the misdeeds of their corrupt leaders, especially since most of the Egyptians were on amicable terms with their Hebrew neighbors. We must remember that in those times individualism was not so prevalent an attitude as it is today. Consequently, peoples more often than individuals were the objects of the Divine wrath. Many believe this tenth plague to have been responsible for the origin of the Feast of the Passover. While it raged, the Hebrew family would select a lamb or a kid from the flock and smear its blood on the lintel or side posts of the door, together with an aromatic plant known as the *hyssop*. When the Lord passed through the territory to inflict His plague, they believed that He would notice this blood and "pass over" the houses of the Israelites which were thereby designated. Another opinion claims that the ritual may have been in use long before the time of the plagues. In this case, its practitioners regarded it as a means of obtaining Divine protection from any crisis or misfortune.

Bibliography

Anderson, W. B.: *Understanding the Old Testament.* Prentice-Hall, New York, 1957.

Andrews, Roy Chapman: *All About Whales.* Random, New York, 1954.

Buchsbaum, R., and Milne, L. J.: *The Lower Animals.* Doubleday, New York, 1960.

Catholic Encyclopedia: Encylopedia Press, New York, 1913.

Catlow, M. E.: *Popular Scripture Zoology.* Reeve, London, 1852.

Clarke, Rev. W. K. L.: *Concise Bible Commentary.* Macmillan, New York, 1953.

Cochran, D. M.: *Living Amphibians of the World.* Doubleday, New York, 1961.

Eiselen, F. C., and Downey, A. G.: *Abingdon Bible Commentary.* Abingdon-Cokesbury, Nashville, Tenn., 1929.

Gilliard, E. T.: *Living Birds of the World.* Doubleday, New York, 1958.

Howells, Victor: *A Naturalist in Palestine.* Melrose, London, 1956.

Jewish Encyclopedia: Funk and Wagnalls, New York, 1901.

Klotz, A. B., and Klots, E. B.: *Living Insects of the World.* Doubleday, New York, 1959.

Kramer, S. N.: *Sumerian Mythology.* Harper, New York, 1961.

Lathrop, Dorothy, and French, Helen: *Animals of the Bible.* Stokes, New York, 1937.

Ley, Wiely: *The Lungfish, The Dodo, and The Unicorn.* Viking, New York, 1948.

Meek, T. J.: *Hebrew Origins.* Harper, New York, 1960.

Miller, Madeleine S., and J. L.: *Harper's Bible Dictionary.* Harper, New York, 1959.

Moscati, S.: *Ancient Semitic Civilizations.* Capricorn Books, New York, 1960.

Norman, J. R., and Fraser, F. G.: *Giant Fishes, Whales and Dolphins.* Putnam, London, 1934.

Parmalee, A.: *All the Birds of the Bible.* Harper, New York, 1959.

Pinney, Roy: *Vanishing Wildlife.* Dodd, Mead, New York, 1963.

Sanderson, Ivan T.: *Living Mammals of the World.* Hanover House, New York, 1955.

Schmidt, K. P., and Inger, R. F.: *Living Reptiles of the World.* Hanover House, New York, 1957.

Stimpson, George W.: *A Book About the Bible.* Harper, New York, 1945.

Terrien, Samuel: *Lands of the Bible.* Simon and Schuster, New York, 1948.

Tristram, Henry B.: *The Natural History of the Bible.* London, 1868.

Universal Jewish Encyclopedia: Funk & Wagnalls, New York, 1948.

Wiley, Lulu Ramsey: *Bible Animals.* Vantage, New York, 1957.

Wood, John George: *Bible Animals.* London, 1869.

Index

ROY PINNEY

Roy Pinney is a native New Yorker, but he has never given in to it. As a combination writer-photographer-naturalist, he has been on some seventy expeditions to all parts of the world.

Born in New York City in 1911, he was the Brooklyn Museum's Curator of Insects while still in his teens and was often in the company of the great wildlife conservationists, Ernest Thompson Seton and William T. Hornaday.

As a war correspondent-photographer, Mr. Pinney covered the Normandy invasion. After the war, he became interested in the possibilities of underwater photography and helped develop much special equipment for it. He also found time to try aerial photography and qualify as a pilot.

He has filmed two television series, "Wild Cargo" and "Wild Kingdom." He and his wife, Doris, a noted photographer in her own right, took the pictures for the animated film "Turn Around—Boys," which won first prize in its category at the 1963 Cannes Film Festival.

Mr. Pinney is founder and past president of the Picture Agency Council of America, founder and trustee of the American Society of Magazine Photographers, and founder and president of Photo-Library, Inc., a world-wide picture agency.

He writes a monthly column for *U.S. Camera* and is the author and illustrator of a number of books, among them, *Advertising Photography*, *Wild Animal Pets*, *The Complete Book of Cave Exploration*, *Vanishing Wildlife*, *Micro-Zoo*, and *Young Israel*.